PHILOSOPHY OF SCIENCE

The Metaphysics
of Logical Positivism

GUSTAV   BERGMANN

Philosophy
of Science

THE UNIVERSITY

OF WISCONSIN PRESS

Madison, 1958

Published by The University of Wisconsin Press,
430 Sterling Court, Madison 6, Wisconsin

Copyright © 1957,
by the Regents of the University of Wisconsin.
Copyright, Canada, 1957.
Distributed in Canada by Burns and MacEachern, Toronto.
Second printing, 1958.

Lithography by Cushing-Malloy, Inc., Ann Arbor, Michigan.
Printed in the United States of America.

Library of Congress Catalog Card Number 57–5237

Preface

This is not the book I planned to write. The book I planned and set out to write was a philosophy of psychology, entitled "The Logic of Behavior." It was to be a volume of moderate size, three to four hundred pages, with an introductory chapter on the philosophy of science and a concluding one on the structural history of ideas in the area since the seventeenth century. As work progressed, it became clear to me that the task required a volume of eight hundred to a thousand pages. Books that thick are onerous. They are hard on the publisher (if any); they are hard on the reader; and the author may not live to complete them. The situation thus demanded a change in plans. This book is what, as a result of that change, has become of the introductory chapter on the philosophy of science. So I shall first say a few words on what sort of book it is and why I believe that it may be of some use.

The literature of the philosophy of science is very large; the number of books is relatively small. There are excellent reasons for that. No one can hope that he will be able to say something both worth while and of his own on all the topics that might legitimately be included in such a book. Even to present decently everything important others have said on them would be a staggering task, requiring many years and several volumes. Accordingly, the best books are almost monographic; the worst ones are as shallow as they are broad. The best policy for a volume of moderate size is, therefore, selection. But then the selection itself becomes a problem. If the author is, as I think he must be, a technical philosopher, he will be tempted to include many traditional subjects of perennial technical interest, say, a chapter on causation, another one on induction, a third on probability, and so on. Some of his prospective readers, even among the more serious ones, will find these chapters too high a fence around those in which they may find what is to them of more immediate interest. One reason why this book may be of some use is that a different principle of selection was given to me by my original purpose. I began by asking myself which more or less philosophical ideas are indispensable for a rather detailed logical analysis of psychology. An exposition of these ideas will be found in the second and third chapters. It will, I hope, be of immediate interest to philosophically minded scientists. The first chapter, in turn, contains the minimum of philosophical ideas that one needs to understand the other two. So it may be of less immediate interest to some. I don't see how that can be helped. The orientation of the whole is toward psychology and the behavior sciences. This is one of the marks the book bears of its origin. Even so, I did not suppress what could be said with a relatively small additional effort about physics. To suppress such passages would have been not only wasteful but also ill-advised. For they contain that bare minimum of the philosophy of physics which, I judge, the philosophical analyst of any science cannot without peril ignore. If my judgment is sound, or if it is at least not too far off, then this is another reason why the book may be of use. Some of these comments on the philosophy of physics are, inevitably, rather condensed, assuming a measure of familiarity with the issues. So are some others on more technical issues within philosophy proper. In a first reading all these comments can be skipped; some readers may rest content to skip them altogether. Since I dislike long footnotes, except in certain special kinds of writing, I marked the passages containing these comments by small print.

Having said that much about the history of the book, I must take time to answer three questions. The first flows from a natural curiosity. The second and third air suspicions which this history cannot fail to arouse.

Liking brief titles as much as I dislike long footnotes, when I first conceived the book which I did not write, I thought of three one-word titles for its three parts: "Foundations" for the introduction which has become this book; "System" for the middle part, which was to be the bulk; "Development" for the historical conclusion. The first question is: Will there be two more books, corresponding to "System" and "Development" respectively? The answer is that I do not know. Time is short. The attractive tasks are many; and the inner forces directing the choice among them, not to mention the outer ones, are not entirely under conscious control. There is also the circumstance that on some, though surely not on all, of the matters to be taken up in those two unwritten books I have already had my say, though surely often not even to my own satisfaction, in a rather large number of essays. However, I do not wish to prepare excuses for myself. I merely wish to say that while I do not promise anything I shall do everything I can.

Does this book stand by itself in content? This is the second question. The proof of the pudding is of course in the eating. But I shall try to turn away some of the wrath which one can, perhaps, not entirely escape if he publishes what *may* be work in progress. An illustration will serve better than generalities. Take the related issues of "Gestalt" and "Reduction." There is a good deal of rather detailed analysis of them in this book. Some, though by no means all, of the examples are taken from psychology. Yet, for all its detail and all the examples, this analysis is merely a "foundation," that is, it deals only with those aspects and parts of the issues that appear in all sciences. If I have done this well, then some readers may be disappointed because I have not also gone into all the twists and facets of the two issues in psychology. Thus they may charge me with presenting a fragment. Such readers I urge to reconsider. To satisfy creditably the appetite aroused in them would take another book, the one corresponding to "system." Nor is that all. Just as a systematic analysis of all those twists and facets is not even possible without the proper foundation, so it is not really satisfactory without numerous hints concerning the structural history of ideas. To explain these hints takes still another book, corresponding to "development." Thus we would be back to the eight hundred or a thousand pages. Nor would there then be a book that may be of some use to those who would not, even if the other volumes existed, reach for them.

Does this book stand by itself in form? This is the third question. I deleted quite a few traces of the original plan. But it seemed more candid as well as more convenient for the reader and myself not to delete all of them. Those left are of two kinds. Throughout the book, especially in the small print, there is a scattering of such sentences as "This question *will* be answered in the second (or in the third) volume." The sentence should be read not as a promise but as an abbreviation for "This question is so complex that, together with others also raised in this book, it *can* not be answered as thoroughly as it should be answered except in the space of two more books." This is the one kind of trace I preserved. The other is the word "work" in the Introduction. Even in this brief preface I had to distinguish among three things: the philosophical questions raised by any science; those peculiar to a particular science; the structural history of philosophical ideas concerning this particular science. The differences and connections among these three things should be explained in any book on the philosophy of science. The best place for this is in the introduction. The best explanation, as of all philosophical matters, is by example, that is, by talking about one particular science. The example I chose is, naturally, psychology. The "work" I mention a few times in the Introduction has therefore three parts, the one book I wrote and the two which I may or may not write. In other words, I left the original introduction virtually unchanged. It could thus serve for all three books, to which accordingly it refers as parts.

One more word about the manner of presentation. Some who read the manuscript praised it for what they kindly called its simplicity and because of the effort I had made to avoid all expendable jargon. Some others disliked the same things so much that they accused me of talking down to the reader. Evoking no echo from a hidden guilt, the accusation leaves me unruffled. I merely tried, in the fumbling way of one not born to the language he writes, to emulate that simplicity which is the distinctive virtue of the British philosophical style. Trying to do this, I also followed the precept of one of the great masters of those who write, philosophy or anything else, in any language. *Plus ce qu'on dit est grand et difficile, plus il faut être simple et sans prétention dans le style.**

* Stendhal, *Correspondence,* October 20, 1816.

ACKNOWLEDGMENTS

THE State University of Iowa awarded me one of its temporary research professorships for the first semester of 1954/55. Thus relieved of all teaching duties, I could finish this book in good time. I am under obligation to the officers of the University who were responsible for this decision.

Professor May Brodbeck of the University of Minnesota helped me by constructing the index. She also read the manuscript, helping me to make it as nearly idiomatic as my stubbornness permitted. The debt of gratitude which I owe her is great.

My wife skillfully and faithfully read the proof.

G.B.

Iowa City
Fall, 1955

Contents

Figures

PHILOSOPHY OF SCIENCE

Introduction

SCIENTISTS observe what happens. Whenever they can, they manipulate things so that they may observe what happens under certain circumstances. This helps them to discover laws of nature. Having discovered some, they try to combine them into theories. Philosophers, even of science, do none of these things. They ask themselves such questions as: What is a law of nature? What is a scientific theory? Scientists, like everybody else, make deductions. For instance, they deduce further laws from a theory which they have constructed from some others. Philosophers of science describe the role deduction plays in science. Philosophy, including the philosophy of science, is thus, unlike science, purely verbal, analytic, and reflective. Perhaps this is why its usefulness is doubted by some at this time and place. Yet nothing would be more foolish than to begin a philosophical book with a defense of its usefulness. Whatever use it has must show itself as it proceeds.

Psychologists, like all other scientists, invent terms or concepts, formulate laws, and construct theories. Such topics as the logic of concept formation and the nature of laws and of theories can therefore not be ignored in the philosophy of psychology. Clearly, they are equally relevant to all other sciences. There is thus a group of problems that arise in the philosophical analysis of any science. This suggests the expository strategy I adopted. The first part of this work deals, selectively, with some topics from the philosophy of science in general. For want of a better name, I have called it *Foundations*. Sometimes I shall speak neutrally in this first part. In discussing some of the puzzles connected with definitions, for instance, nothing is lost by not specifying to which science the concept defined belongs. Something may even be gained. One is forced to distinguish the puzzles that arise in connection with any defined term from those additional ones that seem to arise in connection with some defined terms of psychology. Or, should the difference between these two kinds of puzzles be merely an apparent difference, one is more likely to discover that they are at bottom the same. Such distinctions and such "discoveries" are the stuff of philosophical analysis. There will thus not be much talk about psychology in the first part. But illustrations are useful everywhere;

3

in philosophical discourse they are practically indispensable. Naturally, some illustrations will be drawn from psychology. More often, though, and for a reason that is fairly obvious, they will be taken from the physical sciences. Physics is at present not only the most successful science; it is also logically the most elaborate and complex. Even biology, though less accomplished than physics, far excels in these respects whatever there actually is of a science of behavior. What better place, then, to look for the tools needed in the philosophy of the latter than an analytical description of the former?

The procedure I chose may seem reasonable. It is nonetheless far from uncontroversial. A critic may point out that it rests on what critics like to call unexamined assumptions or presuppositions. The way the words 'assumption' and 'presupposition' are used in philosophical discourse is far from clear. I would therefore not use them myself without first analyzing them. Moreover, if this were the place for their analysis, I believe I could show that they serve no good purpose. Yet I believe I know what the critic has in mind. My unexamined assumption is, presumably, that there are no "logical" differences between physics and psychology. After a fashion I agree. Only, and this shows part of what is wrong with the logic of 'assumption', it does not follow that I must therefore separately and explicitly "prove" my "assumption," either at the very beginning or at least later on. All I need do and all I shall do is to present an analysis of the logical problems of psychology. This I shall do in the second part of this work, which I called *System*. The name does not please me at all. It sounds stuffy and it has, in the history of psychology, some rather unfortunate associations. But I cannot think of another single word that serves.

Of course I shall not explicitly and separately prove the adequacy of the analysis in the second part. If that were necessary, would it not also be necessary to prove the adequacy of the proof? But let us not be too hasty. Two brief comments now may save much trouble later. They concern two distinctions that are both essential to my plan. One is the distinction between science and philosophy, which we have already encountered. The other is the distinction between the philosophy of science and philosophy proper.

'Proof' and 'proving' have more than one meaning. A mathematician who uses them means one thing. A scientist who, having proposed a theory, presents as proof the factual evidence for it means something else. When a philosopher has finished an analysis, he can do something about it which is still different but which one may, if one wishes, call proving it, though I myself would rather not overwork this word. The philosopher may, and I think should, review alternative analyses that have been offered as well as the criticisms that have been raised against his own. This review will consist of two parts, of which the first is essential, the second supplementary.

The first is the actual refutation of these criticisms and those alternative analyses, showing where and why they err. Such refutation operates of course within the philosopher's own position. Nobody can do anything else; whoever thinks that he can merely deludes himself. The supplement is an attempt to understand why these errors were made at all and why they did not seem to be errors to those who made them. I shall in the second part (as well as in the third) review the main types of alternatives and criticisms. This sort of thing is indeed the very flesh on the bare bones of philosophical analysis. Scientists do not need to bother with this dialectic. This is one of the characteristic differences between philosophy and science.

There are then philosophical positions which one cannot transcend any more than one can help believing what he believes. (One can of course be critical of one's self and be fair and tolerant toward others. But these are attitudes toward beliefs, one's own and others'.) Are there, then, also positions in the philosophy of science? This brings me to the distinction between philosophy and the philosophy of science. Perhaps it is not sharp; its edges, like those of many others, may be blurred. That is nothing to worry about or to apologize for. Generally, labels or, as I like to call them, chapter heading words are not worth arguing for or against. The only question is whether they are useful. These two, I think, are of some use in explaining the plan and the limitations of this work.

Scientists know how to use such words as 'electron', 'friction coefficient', and 'specific weight'. They agree on the circumstances under which statements in which these words occur are true or false, as the case may be. Suppose somebody is puzzled by that. The reason for his puzzlement, he tells us, is that neither he nor anybody else has ever "seen" an electron or a friction coefficient or a specific weight. One way of solving his problem is to ask him to name the sorts of things he believes he and others do see. He mentions physical objects, some properties of them such as colors, and some relations among them such as spatial ones, adding that since he has seen such things, statements in which their names occur do not puzzle him the way he is puzzled by statements in which electrons, friction coefficients, and specific weights are mentioned. We now point out to him that such terms as 'electron', 'friction coefficient', and 'specific weight' can be so defined that all terms * occurring in their definitions are of the kind he accepts. Hence, since a defined term is merely an abbreviation that can be eliminated, the terms that raised a philosophical question in his mind are really as unproblematic as those that did not. Suppose that our friend is satisfied with this analysis but that somebody else, who was struck by the same problem, when asked what he thinks he and others "see," gives us a different answer. He insists that he does not really see trees or stones but merely what he calls mental contents, stone percepts, tree percepts, and so

* Except the logical ones such as 'and', 'is', 'all'. See p. 20.

on. To this man we could say that now the shoe is on the other foot, for we do not understand what he says since we do not understand how he uses 'see'. We know perfectly well the difference between a tree and a tree percept; we also know that we see the former through or by means of the latter; but it makes no sense to say that one sees the latter. Literally we would be right if we said all this. Some philosophers would indeed have saved themselves much trouble if they had realized what extraordinary uses they sometimes make of very ordinary words such as, in this case, the verbs of perception. Only, I think it would be a mistake to dismiss our second friend's reply on this ground alone. He may have a point. Let us then accept his answer, if only to ask him something in turn. Can he explain how we know how to use 'tree' and 'stone'? Our question, it will be noticed, is quite similar to the one from which both our friends started, namely, how scientists know how to use such terms as 'electron', 'friction coefficient', and 'specific weight'. Accordingly, the answer the second may give us is quite similar to the one we ourselves gave to the first questioner. He may say he believes that such terms as 'tree' and 'stone' can be so defined that all terms in their definitions refer only to what he "sees." Accepting this for the sake of the argument, we point out that he already had the key to the original problem, concerning electrons and friction coefficients, which had them both puzzled. To put it briefly, if 'electron' can be defined in terms of 'stone' and 'stone' in terms of 'stone percept', then 'electron', too, can be defined in terms of 'stone percept'. Suppose our second friend is satisfied with this answer to his original question.

The two disagree on what we "see." They agree that we do not see such things as friction coefficients and that our not seeing them gives rise to a philosophical question. But they can, within certain limits, also agree on how to answer this question. Originally problematic terms become for both of them unproblematic if they can be so defined that all the terms in their definitions are unproblematic. Thus they can agree that much is gained if the terms of science are being "traced down" to a "lower level," even though this level be unproblematic to only one of them. This task they assign to the philosophy of science; the issue on which they disagree, to philosophy proper. (Some may wish to describe the division by saying that the level on which in this case agreement ends is that of "common sense realism" and that the philosophy of science does not and need not examine its "presuppositions.") This shows, in one rather crucial instance, how the representatives of quite different philosophical positions may yet agree within the limits of the philosophy of science. But one must not overlook that still other positions may not even accept the method of explication by definition which is at the root of this particular agreement. I do not happen to know such a position; at least I know none that I would take very seriously. But let us be fair and count this possibility as a blurred edge. Let us look at another.

Scientists, as I mentioned before, try to make interesting deductions. Philosophers of science describe the role deduction plays in science. The nature of deductive inference, i.e., of logic in the technical sense of the term, is a problem of philosophy proper. Thus it would seem that one could take quite different positions in the philosophy of logic and yet agree on its place in science. By and large this is so. For instance, whether a certain inference is of the kind called deductive is in most cases quite uncontroversial. However, there are also some other cases. The disagreements concerning them are recondite and subtle; I could not discuss them here without writing a book quite different from the one I am writing. Yet these differences may and, I think, sometimes do influence one's account of the place of logic in science. At least they influence its "style." There is another blurred edge. Perhaps the blur is particularly large in the case of a linguistic philosopher like myself. Such a one finds it very hard to say anything worth while about science without first saying a good deal about logic. Nor does he find it easy to say anything worth while about logic without making some points that belong to philosophy proper. There will be a measure of this sort of thing in the first part. Even so, I hope I have made it plausible, though I have of course not proved it—the proof of this pudding, too, is in the eating—that there is an area or group of interrelated problems which one may reasonably set aside as the philosophy of science and that this area is much less controversial than philosophy proper. As to the latter, I made a very strict rule for myself. I shall say what is necessary, sometimes marking these statements for what they are lest there be any doubt or confusion. But I shall abstain from supporting them by the sort of detailed and often very technical argument that belongs to philosophy proper. For, again, if I did this, I would be writing a different book.

The second part, too, will have its share of philosophy proper. The analysis of psychology it contains is of the kind called behavioristic, that is, it seems to deny the existence of mental contents. I say seems because if such an analysis is done well then one sees that it does not really deny that there are mental contents; it merely ignores them, and even that only after a fashion. As far as the science of psychology is concerned one can, as we shall see, let it go at that. But this leaves one intellectually uneasy. We all know in a commonsensical way that we all have mental contents. Thus one should like to see accurately and nicely how that knowledge "fits" with the behavioristic analysis. This is of course a philosophical need, just as the problems one must solve in order to satisfy it are philosophical problems; for that phrase, 'the existence of mental contents', commonsensical as it sounds and is, is yet fraught with philosophical problems. They are, not surprisingly, those one must solve if one wants to produce the fit. Psychologists who write about the philosophy of their field (they usually call themselves methodologists) often shirk this task; even more often they say a lot of nonsense about it. Here, then, is a job for the philosopher. I shall not shirk it.

Logical analysis, we saw, has a dialectical side, the analysis or, as I just called it, the review of alternative analyses and of criticisms. This dialectic has a historical dimension. A scientist may be a better man if he knows the history of his science; he is not therefore a better scientist. Again there are differences. In physics the store of factual information is so vast, the power and logical complexity of current theory so great that history hardly adds anything to the guidance these facts and theories provide for the researcher. This holds not only for the daily routine; it also holds, or so I believe, for the great innovators of the first half of this century. In the fledgling behavior sciences things are different. If the facts are either obscure or not yet organized by theory, it may be useful to know which facts stirred the imaginations of one's predecessors. If there is as yet no theory or not much of one, the concepts with which others tried to build theories in the past may be suggestive. Thus progress may be facilitated or, at least, waste may be avoided by a knowledge of history. If the behavior sciences are in the middle, philosophy is at the other extreme from physics. Since there are "positions" in philosophy, since one cannot "learn" it as one learns a science, some think that it does not advance at all and that "objectively" one can do no more than attempt a history and, perhaps, a taxonomy of the several positions. There is a kernel of truth in this view, as in the eternal jokes about one's mother-in-law. Like these jokes it is grossly exaggerated. In one sense, it is true that a philosophical proposition cannot, like one of mathematics or science, be established by proof or by an appeal to experience. For is it not, among other things, the task of philosophy to elucidate what is meant by 'proof' and 'experience'? In one sense, it is therefore also true that philosophical discussion must somewhere come to an end and that "ultimately" the several positions cannot communicate with each other. In another sense, this is a dangerous half-truth. The art is to push toward the horizon that point where talk must cease. In fact, philosophers of different positions have always talked with each other and learned from each other. In this sense, there is progress in philosophy. The best comparison is, perhaps, with chess. One learns how to play chess by playing it, but also by studying the games of the masters. In this way one learns what alternatives there are, the gambits and what they imply, which patterns lead to which others. Similarly, one learns how to philosophize by philosophizing, but also by studying the thought of the masters.

It is clear, I trust, that the history I am speaking about is not that purely factual history honorably and (up to a point) usefully pursued by those who search for unedited manuscripts, establish texts, and compile biographies. Nor is it the enterprise of those who trace influences, that is, who try to combine the bare facts with bits of psychological and sociological knowledge or insight into hypotheses, e.g., that somebody thought or wrote something because he had read the books of somebody else, or because he found himself with certain motives, intellectual or otherwise, in a certain intellectual or social situation. What I am speaking about is structural history which, in a sense, is neither factual nor causal. Rather, it is a comparative analysis of ideas in their logical interdependence. To be sure, the edges of this distinction, too, are blurred. It is really more a matter of emphasis. And the structural historian must be very careful lest he either claim too much or deceive himself and others about what he is doing. Suppose he studies two systems of ideas, L and F, discovering that parts of the first logically either imply or suggest parts of the other. This is what he is really interested in. Yet he does not call the two systems L and F; he calls them the ideas of Leibniz and of Fechner. Here his troubles begin. For one thing, it is often very difficult to find out what the ideas of dead people actually were, even if they wrote books. (Sometimes it is not easy when the authors are still alive.) To discover them, as well as we may, we often need the help of factual and causal historians. For another, even if we have got hold of the ideas of the man Leibniz and the man Fechner and if there is a logical connection of one sort or another between them, it does not follow that there was also a causal connection. These are the predicaments and limitations of structural history. They are severe indeed. Yet its advantages more than make up for them. For one thing, it has an intrinsic interest. I explained this before, when I used the comparison with chess. For another, it is indispensable in the causal reconstruction of the development. Now I am as sceptical as anybody about the extent and the reliability of our causal knowledge of the past. As will transpire, I could not judge otherwise, from where I stand, as long as the behavior sciences are not more advanced than they are. After all, knowledge of causes and knowledge of laws and theories are virtually the same thing. Of course, this does not mean that one should not pursue causal history. It is of intrinsic interest; and it is foolish not to do what is worth doing in itself as well as one can merely because one cannot do it as well as one might wish. On the other hand, little as we may know, it is more than plausible, or, to put it more cautiously, it is the best guess available that the logical connections of ideas are among the causes of their appearance, ascendency, and decline. Notice that I say causes, not cause. To believe that they are the sole cause is the fallacy of rationalism. (This is one of the many meanings of that glittering word, 'rationalism'.) But to believe that they are not among the causes, however fashionable it may be at the moment, is an irrationalism little short of hysteria. If this is so, then the structural history of ideas more than pays its way, even from the viewpoint of the factual and causal historian.

The third part of this work attempts a structural history of the philosophy of psychology. Starting with the time when what is so clumsily called the modern frame of reference took shape in the works of such men as Galileo, Descartes, Hobbes, Newton, and Locke, it spans about three hundred years. Searching again for a single word to name this part, I finally chose *Development*. One reason I avoided 'history' is that I wanted to avoid the associations of scholarship it evokes, the sort of scholarship of which E. G. Boring's volumes are a distinguished example. I am a philosophical analyst, not a scholar; and I am not, except as a consumer and perhaps as an occasional amateur, interested in scholarship. This is therefore primarily a work of philosophical analysis. Only, such analysis finds its natural supplement in the structural history of ideas.

Until rather recently, philosophy and psychology were cultivated by the same people. Reading their books, one finds it often hard to tell where what we would nowadays call either the one or the other begins and where it leaves off. Sometimes the same passage is a mixture of both. If one could still ask these writers which was which, some might not even understand the question. This is no longer so. Psychology, at least in this country, has found itself as a science. But even now psychologists are very much interested in the philosophy of their field. Usually they call it methodology. Not infrequently they even dabble in philosophy proper, for the most part without knowing it, which does not at all improve their performance since, to stay with my metaphor, they do not even know the opening moves of the game. Partly this may be a historical hangover. Mostly, I think, it is the result of frustration and of the wishful thinking it engenders in some. When the going in the field is hard, as it is in the field of psychology, one looks for a short cut. The philosophy of science, or of any science, is not a realistic short cut to achievements in this science. All the analyst can do for the scientist's actual progress is to keep him out of the dead alleys of intellectual confusion. This, however, is not to say that as long as the scientific character of a field is not fully understood by some, methodological awareness may not be a considerable advantage in the field itself. The recent history of psychology seems to bear this out. Under the circumstances philosophy proper will have to appear in the third part, too. One can no more analyze the empiricism-nativism issue without at least some reference to Kant's philosophy of space than one can understand the psychological ideas of the classical British writers without some grasp of what they tried to do in philosophy proper.

The task is virtually beyond human strength. Naturally, then, I shall operate within certain limits, those I impose upon myself and those my limitations impose upon me. As for the former, take the case of Leibniz. The connections I mentioned before exist, logically as well as, probably, causally. Nor need a contemporary analyst be a historical scholar to know something about Leibniz's ideas. They are structurally too interesting and too important for that. Unfortunately, though, they are so complex and their grasp requires so much knowledge of philosophy proper that I could not possibly deal with them in this work except in the most superficial manner. Sometimes I shall be forced to do just that. Wherever it is possible without distorting the picture I shall in such cases observe a decent silence. On the other hand, I shall not abstain from occasional remarks about the interactions of psychological ideas with the general cultural context. That I have no illusions about the knowledge claim of such "insights" I have said before. If one does not have such illusions, there is no harm in this intellectual game. At least it creates a picture that produces "understanding." (What 'understanding' means we shall have to take up in the second part.)

I have talked about history and about philosophy proper. Finally, poor psychology itself ought to be mentioned in this introduction. If one sets out to analyze the logic of physics, he must know some physics. If one wants to analyze the logic of psychology, he must know some psychology. How much is difficult to say, though I would not necessarily say the more the better. There is somewhere a point of diminishing return. Fortunately, there is no danger that I know too much. I am no more a professional psychologist than a professional scholar. I can only hope that I shall muddle through.

CHAPTER ONE

Deduction and definition

TWO KINDS OF WORDS

SUPPOSE Olaf is a cat and consider the words 'Olaf', 'cat', 'mammal'. Consider, on the other hand, the words 'and', 'is', and 'all'. There is a clearly felt difference between these two groups of words (terms). This leads to two questions. First, one will want to know what the difference is; that is, one will want to state adequately the ground of this distinction which we feel so clearly after it has once been called to our attention. Second, one will wonder whether each word belongs to either the one or the other of these two kinds. If one had reason to believe that the answer to the second question is negative, the first would lose some of its interest. If the answer should turn out to be affirmative, one may have got hold of a very fundamental distinction. But one must, of course, start with the first question. One answer to it is that each word of the first group, 'Olaf', 'cat', 'mammal', refers to something—some thing—or names something while there is nothing a word of the second group refers to or names. This is indeed the best way to state the difference succinctly. It also explains why the words of the first kind are called *descriptive* or *referential*. They name, in Berkeley's memorable phrase, the furniture of the world. Yet there are difficulties; perhaps better, there are, as with any succinct formula, possibilities of misunderstanding. To explore the former in order to forestall the latter is the one thing one can do to explicate a philosophical distinction. This is part of the dialectical character of philosophy.

Here is one difficulty. 'Olaf' and 'cat' do not name the same sort of "thing." Olaf is a physical object; cat is a kind of physical object, or, what amounts to the same thing, to be a cat is a property of a physical object, just as it is a property of some such objects to be black. As it happens, some cats are black, that is, some physical objects are instances of both kinds or, as one says, they exemplify both properties. Ordinary language does not use 'kind' and 'property' quite synonymously. We would rather say that cats are a kind and that to be green is a property than say it the other way round. I am not now concerned with this "felt difference." Aside from it, 'kind' and 'property' stand for the same idea. 'Character' is another word one may use to express it. The difference between 'Olaf' and 'cat' is, then, that while the former names a physical object, the latter names a character. What makes this a real difference is that while one can point at a physical object, one cannot in the same sense point at a character; one can merely point at an instance of it, that is, at a physical object that exemplifies it. This suggests a division among descriptive words, namely, *character words* and *proper names*. 'Concept' is frequently so used that it becomes synonymous with 'character word'. Proper names refer to what can be pointed at. I put it this way, speaking of what can be pointed at rather than of physical objects, because one may disagree on what can actually be pointed at and yet agree that the difference between what can and what cannot be singled out by pointing is important. If one thinks it important, he may come to feel that 'Olaf' and 'cat' do not name or refer in the same sense. Such a one may wish to distinguish between different kinds of naming or referring and, in the course of making the distinction, specialize his use of 'naming', 'referring', and whatever other words, such as 'denoting', he needs for his special purpose. Some philosophers seem to believe that if one pursues this line of thought, our original distinction between the words that do and those that do not name becomes questionable. I disagree. Surely, there is a difference between character words and proper names; but there is no difference in the way they name. He who believes that there is has been misled by the metaphor of pointing. I call it a metaphor because, though I know of no better way to indicate what is involved, eventually the distinction between proper names and concepts must be made in grammatical terms. But of this later (p. 42).

Another difficulty seems at first sight more serious. Take 'mermaid'. Nobody will doubt that if each word is to belong to one of the two groups, then 'mermaid' belongs with 'Olaf', 'cat', and 'mammal' rather than with 'and', 'is', and 'all'. What then does it name? If one feels embarrassed by this question, he may try to rule such words as 'mermaid' and 'centaur' out of the language; or, to use a term which is much overworked and I think rightly discredited, he may call them meaningless. This would be a mistake. We all understand the sentence 'There are no mermaids'; we even know that it is true. Thus there would be a sentence that is certainly meaningful, since it is even true, and that would yet contain a meaningless word. The notions of meaning and truth are no doubt difficult and in need of analysis; but surely no plausible analysis of them could ever yield this sort of thing, a true sentence containing a meaningless word. Thus one cannot avoid bracketing 'mermaid' and 'centaur' with 'cat' and 'black', in spite of the fact that there are no mermaids or centaurs and that, therefore, in a sense they do not name anything. Fortunately, there is no real difficulty. We cannot point at green or cat any more than at mermaid or centaur. We can only point at instances of the first two characters. Since the second two have no instances, there is quite naturally nothing at all we could point at in their case. As far as it goes, this reminder helps. But it does not go far enough; some dissatisfaction remains. To dispel it, another distinction must be introduced. 'Green' and 'black' name simple characters; 'cat' and 'mermaid', irrespective of the circumstance that there are cats while there are no mermaids, are both names of complex characters. The basic idea is that complex characters are combinations of simple ones. If one wishes, one can so arrange one's language that the difference corresponds to that between *defined* and *undefined* descriptive terms; simple characters being named by undefined descriptive terms, a complex character by a defined descriptive term, the definition itself specifying how the former combine into the latter. For an undefined character word to make sense, there indeed must be a character which it names and with which we are *directly acquainted*. Nor can one be directly acquainted with a character without being so acquainted with at least one instance of it. A blind man born blind does not know what 'green' means. An undefined character word therefore names something in a sense in which a defined one does not, irrespective of whether the complex character which the latter "names" does, as in the case of 'cat', or does not, as in the case of 'mermaid', have instances. If one wishes, one may say that defined and undefined character words do not "name" or "refer" in the same sense. The difference makes no trouble for our original distinction between descriptive words and that other kind which I have as yet not named. It merely suggests that we at first limit this distinction to the undefined terms of a language. This is indeed technically the proper way to introduce it. Afterwards one extends it to all terms, calling a defined term descriptive if and only if at least one undefined descriptive term occurs in its definition. If one proceeds in this manner, 'mermaid' and 'centaur' become again descriptive.

Proper names, being undefined, do not give rise to problems comparable to that caused by 'mermaid'. But one may profitably ask two questions. How about 'Hamlet'? And how about such phrases as 'the wife of Smith', which we use instead of proper names? As to 'Hamlet', the word does indeed not name anything. Whether or not there was once upon a time a Nordic prince of similar name and fate is, of course, beside the point, as are those complicated conventions by virtue of which we use and understand the names of fictional people and other objects of our imagination. More to the point, one does get into philosophical trouble if one uses words purporting to be proper names without being directly acquainted with what they name, just as one would if one used words purporting to be undefined character words without being directly acquainted with the character they name. For instance, in a properly functioning language a proper name should combine with a character word into a properly functioning sentence and such a sentence should be either true or false, or, what amounts to the same thing, either it or its negation should be true. Yet it is against the grain to say that either 'Hamlet is (was) blond' or 'Hamlet is (was) not blond' is true. The case of such phrases as 'the wife of Smith', which are technically known as *definite descriptions,* is not different. Literally, they are not proper names; for a proper name is merely a pointer, a spoken gesture, as it were, while a descriptive phrase says something about what it purports to point at, for instance that it is the wife of Smith. Yet a descriptive phrase can get us into trouble quite similar to that caused by 'Hamlet'. If, for instance, Smith is a bachelor, then it is equally silly to insist on the truth of either 'The wife of Smith is blond' or 'The wife of Smith is not blond'. Definite descriptions are nevertheless indispensable, for they enable us, in those cases in which they do not backfire, to speak of what is not in front of our nose. So we cannot get along without them, or without a circumscription or substitute for them, in any language. Russell discovered a circumscription that can in any context be substituted for a definite description without causing any trouble. Of this later (p. 47).

We have come upon another fundamental idea, that of a properly functioning language. Part of the idea is, obviously, that speaking such a language would keep one out of philosophical trouble. Equally obviously, since we all are in philosophical trouble, whether we know it or not, English or, for that matter, any other natural language does not always function properly. Also, it would seem that to reflect on what such a language would be like is a rather effective method of philosophizing. I just used it myself in two instances. First, I stated what is known as the *Principle of Acquaintance*: In a properly functioning language an undefined descriptive term, whether proper name or character word, occurs only if the speaker is directly acquainted with what it names. Second, I have shown that in a properly functioning language definite descriptions have to be reworded. As it recurs, I shall explore this idea of an "improved" language further and explain it in greater detail. For the time being I merely wish to mark its first appearance. Let us now take up the main line of thought where we left it.

I am attempting to establish a dichotomy among all words. A word either does or does not name something. 'Olaf' certainly does; 'and' certainly does not. But in other cases the decision is less clear. My procedure has been to consider such cases. I select words not quite like those which clearly name something but which fit even less with those which clearly do not name anything. Then I explain the decision to call them descriptive by explaining, among other things, what one may reasonably mean by 'naming'. We saw, for instance, that a word may "name" a complex character that has no instances. There are two more such decisions to be made and explained. But it will pay if we first consider a certain awkwardness. One might argue as follows. A word is a name if and only if there is something it names. "Which words name?" and "What is there?" (or

"What exists?") are therefore merely two variants of one question. It would be simpler as well as more straightforward to tackle the second variant first. The argument is not convincing. For one thing, we do want to say that a certain word names a complex character which is not exemplified. But if we speak as the tongue runs we also want to say on occasion that this particular character does not "exist." This shows that the two questions, which words name something and what there is or exists, are not the same. Nor is the latter query simpler than the former. Naturally, its difficulty is not one of fact; it is philosophical. The problem is to discover what the question means. What makes this difficult is the blur that surrounds 'there is' and 'exists'. To remove that blur, we shall first have to discuss the words which do not name anything. This is the awkwardness which bedevils us at the moment; for, though they are not the same, the two questions, which words name and what exists, are indeed related. Another order of exposition may have saved us this particular bedevilment; it would certainly have produced another. A philosopher, it has been said, is like a sailor who must repair his vessel while it sails. This, too, is part of the dialectical character of philosophy. Now for the two decisions that remain.

The first concerns *relational characters*. Take 'this circle is inside that triangle' or 'this book is on that table'. The question is what, if anything, is named by 'being inside' or by 'being on'? But first some preliminary remarks are in order. Notice that I am taking the liberty of asking my question about English phrases instead of, literally, words. One good reason for not bothering with this difference is that English itself is not consistent, expressing a relation sometimes by one word as in 'Mary loves Peter', sometimes by a phrase as in our two illustrations or, for that matter, in 'Mary is in love with Peter', just as a nonrelational character is sometimes expressed by a noun, sometimes by an adjective, sometimes still differently. Notice next that relations do not necessarily obtain between two things. Betweenness (of points on a line) is a relation among three. Accordingly, one distinguishes two-term, three-term, four-term relations, and so on. When there is no need to distinguish, I shall from now on speak of both relations and properties as characters. Relations, in turn, are sometimes called relational properties. Linguistically, the difference expresses itself in the number of subjects the character word requires to make a sentence. Character words are also called descriptive predicates. Speaking of subjects instead of, say, in the two-term case, of a subject and an object, I have again taken certain liberties with ordinary grammar. The reasons are by and large the same as before. An "improved" language would not make these distinctions at all or it would make different ones. Strictly speaking, the qualification 'descriptive' in 'descriptive predicate' is necessary; for there are also nondescriptive predicates which do not name anything. But I shall omit the adjective whenever the context leaves no doubt or when the difference makes no difference.

Relational predicates name relations, just as nonrelational ones name properties. With some relations, as with some properties, we are directly acquainted. Some relations, like some properties, are complex; some others, like some other properties, are simple. Linguistically, there is again the difference between defined and undefined relational predicates. Some defined nonrelational predicates are *implicitly relational,* that is, their definitions contain relational predicates. 'Being married', for instance, is explicitly nonrelational since it requires only one subject, e.g., 'John is married'. 'Being married *to',* on the other hand, is a two-term predicate since it requires two subjects, e.g., 'John is married to Jean'. Yet the former can be defined in terms of the latter. The definition is simple indeed: *'x* is married' for 'there is somebody *to* whom *x* is married'. The implicitly relational nature of some other predicates is less obvious.

I do not see how one can deny or even doubt that a relational predicate names something in exactly the same sense in which a nonrelational one does. Clearly, this is a mistake. Yet this was an issue in philosophy proper, and a momentous one at that, the repercussions of which in the philosophy of science were equally momentous. One should therefore try to understand. Some people believe or speak as if they believed that what there is or exists (and, therefore, can have a name) can also be pointed at. If, for instance, such a one also believes that only physical objects can be pointed at, he must consistently hold that only physical objects exist. How adequate or inadequate this notion of existence is, is at the moment beside the point. The point is that if one holds on this ground that relational predicates do not name anything then he must consistently also hold that nonrelational ones do not name anything. One can, as we saw, not point at a property; one can only point at an object that exemplifies it. Nor can one, of course, point at a relation; but one can, say, in the case of a two-term relation, point at any two objects that exemplify it. There is no difference whatsoever. This was not always understood. Apparently it is easier to believe, however mistakenly, that while pointing at a green object one points at green than it is to believe that one points at far when one points, perhaps successively or with two fingers, at two objects that are far apart. This, I think, explains that momentous mistake. Let me add that if I had wanted to sound familiar and, perhaps, more impressive to some, I could have spoken of what is localized in space and time instead of what can be pointed at. This would not have improved what I said. It would merely have enriched the stew by bringing in two difficult notions. But there is some connection.

Now for the last group of words that do, in a reasonable sense, name something. Usually they are called "abstract." Since they abound in science, since the problems of the nonscientific ones among them are really not different, and since we are primarily interested in science, let us choose our illustrations accordingly. Take 'friction coefficient' and 'force'. ('Electron', which I mentioned earlier, is a special case with which we need not bother at this point.) The doubt some people have whether at all or in what sense abstract concepts name anything stems in part from the confusion that surrounds 'abstract'. As it is used, this word has at least three meanings. Nothing is wrong with any of them; but everything may and probably will go wrong if one uses without knowing it one and the same word equivocally. (1) Sometimes 'abstract' is used as if every word that does not refer to a physical object were abstract. (2) Sometimes it is used as if every word naming something with which we are not directly acquainted were abstract. In this sense terms are even called "more" or "less" abstract. What is involved is apparently some vaguely felt distance from the "perceptual level"—a notion about which I shall presently say something. (3) Sometimes 'abstract' is used as if every defined term were abstract. Again, there seem to be degrees of this kind of abstractness, depending on the complexity of the definition or perhaps, if intermediate definitions are used, on the "length" of the definitional chain. These three meanings are not only different; they sometimes collide, which does not at all improve matters. In sense (1) 'cat' and 'green' as well as 'between' are abstract, though apparently the latter, being relational, is, in a still different sense of 'more', thought to be more so; just as some think, I do not know on what grounds, that a "property" such as 'green' is more abstract than a "kind" such as 'cat'. Be that as it may, calling either 'cat' or 'green' or 'between' abstract is probably due to some sort of unanalyzed identification of what is not abstract (and hence concrete), of what exists, and of what is a physical object. In sense (2) neither 'cat' nor 'green' nor 'between' is abstract provided one grants, as we saw one may and does in the philosophy of science, that we are directly acquainted with physical objects, some of their properties, and some relations among them. Again, a term may be abstract in sense (3) and not abstract in sense (2). For instance, we are immediately acquainted with both leftness and rightness; yet 'being to the left of' is easily defined in terms of 'being to the right of' ('x is to the left of y' for 'y is to the right of x'), and conversely. This should suffice to show what a confused, confusing, and, worst of all, useless notion "abstractness" really is. As to the terms usually so called, (a) they are either relational or implicitly relational (e.g., 'boiling point'); (b) they are defined; (c) they do not name things anybody is likely to claim he is directly acquainted with. As for their naming something, we have at this point no difficulty whatsoever. The so-called abstract concepts are just defined predicates. Undefined predicates, whether relational or nonrelational, are names in the most literal sense; and I explained why it makes sense to say that the defined ones, too, name something when we discussed 'mermaid'. The only difference between 'mermaid' and 'force' is this. If the former were exemplified, as it is not, it would be exemplified by a physical object. The latter is exemplified by a pattern, namely, two physical objects, the one accelerated with respect to the other. This is putting it crudely indeed; for 'acceleration' itself is complex and there are clocks and yardsticks involved. However, crude as it is, it will do. The one point I now wish to make about "abstract concepts" is clear. To be sure, there are other points; they will be made in their places.

The prospects of the dichotomy we are trying to establish look bright indeed. We have seen that each in several very broad classes of terms does, in a reasonable sense, refer to something. To establish it even more firmly and thus to complete the analysis, we shall have to examine the words which I claim do not name anything. But it will pay to interrupt again in order to say something about a notion that has already been introduced.

Several times and at rather crucial places of the argument I spoke of our being *directly acquainted* with something. This does not throw our inquiry into the scientific field known as the psychology of perception. Some philosophers have thought so; psychologists are especially prone to make this mistake. Yet it is a mistake and it is important to grasp firmly why it is one. In ordinary speech we use 'seeing', 'perceiving', and perhaps even the somewhat stilted 'being directly acquainted with' very broadly, very fluidly, and more or less synonymously. On ordinary occasions this causes no trouble. Psychologists also use 'perceiving' as a technical term. Thus they might think that I used 'being directly acquainted with' as they use 'perceive'. This is not so (and its not being so is the reason for my choice of the stilted phrase). The way I used it we are directly acquainted only with a class of things so narrowly limited that there is no possible doubt or question when one says, commonsensically, that we are in fact acquainted with them. There are, we saw, those philosophers—it will transpire, though only much later, that after a fashion I am one of them—who insist that we are not directly acquainted with anything but mental contents. Clearly, these people do not use the phrase commonsensically. That does not mean that they do not have a philosophical problem. These problems were discovered through the inadvertent noncommonsensical or "philosophical" use of ordinary words. The philosophical analyst is aware of the difference between the two ways of using words. His very method of solving his problems depends on it. The third way of using words is scientific. Let me show, then, as I set out to do, that the psychologist does not use 'perceiving' as I use 'being directly acquainted with'. The only reasonably specific way in which he can use it and in which he does in fact use it is this. Perception is an adequate and more or less immediate response to physical objects and their properties and relations, no matter how simple or complex the pattern may be. The response is adequate if, verbalized, it states what is actually there—within certain limits and under certain conditions whose specification is of great interest to the psychologist but not to us, at least not right now. The response being immediate excludes situations in which one first "looks" and then "figures" from what one has "seen." The level of perception depends notoriously on motivation and training. Some traffic policemen "see" that a car's speed is one mile above the legal limit. If we were, as I used the word, directly acquainted with such things as speeds of thirty-one miles per hour, I could have saved myself much of the trouble about "abstract" concepts. But this is merely a minor point, telling as I think it is. The heart of the matter is that the psychologist, like everybody else, takes for granted what there is, commonsensically, and therefore is there to be perceived, though if in doubt or when it is a matter of precision he may use instruments or ask the physical scientist. But philosophy is no more physics than it is psychology. Nor does physics rest on the psychology of perception any more than the other way round. Both of them, like all sciences, take common sense for granted, rest on it, and are, so to speak, its long arm. The physicist, for instance, tells us about many things that are there of which common sense knows nothing. This shows what I mean when I say that science is its long arm. But the physicist does not explore what, if anything, it means to say that something "is there" or "exists," whether forces and other "abstract" things exist in the same sense in which physical objects do, and so on. This shows what I mean when I say that science takes common sense for granted. In short, the scientist does not deal with those problems that were first discovered through the inadvertent "philosophical" use of language. This is the task of the philosophical analyst. But let this, too, be clearly understood. In performing this task the analyst does not penetrate "beneath" common sense, does not discover its "foundations" or "presuppositions." I, for one, do not know what the metaphors mean on this occasion. Linguistically this shows itself in the circumstance that the analyst himself does not *use* any word "philosophically"; he merely *mentions* such uses in order to analyze them, thus getting at the core of the problems which they indicate but cannot solve. Nor does he become a scientist when one of the words he either uses or mentions is also used as a technical term in science. In our case, nothing I said has anything to do with the psychology of perception. Not unnaturally, some psychologists find it difficult to keep this distinction always clearly in mind. That is why I am so emphatic.

Now for the other side of the dichotomy, the words that do not name anything. They are called *logical*. The name indicates the important role they play in logical or deductive inference. But before we investigate that role, we had better look at these words by themselves. To speak again as the tongue runs, there are cats and forces and there could be mermaids; there are no "ands" in the world and there could not be, though there are of course kinds of words, among them 'and', and their instances, uttered, written, printed, or what not. Perhaps this is self-evident. To me it is. But even the evident one should fix in one's mind by reflecting on how it fits with other things. Take 'and', then, and consider two sentences, 'It is cold and it is windy' (we would rather say 'It is cold and windy', but this is merely a stylistic nicety) and 'Today is Friday and Peter loves Mary'. If we heard the second in an ordinary conversation we would be baffled. We do not ordinarily mention together what does not, as one says, hang together. There are, of course, many ways in which facts may hang together and one can state these connections. A fact, by the way, as I use 'fact', is what is stated by a sentence, just as a thing, as I use 'thing', is what is named by a word (or phrase). In our illustrations, 'It is often windy when it is cold in our part of the world', which is true, and 'Peter loves Mary because today is Friday', which is rather blatantly false, state such connections. The point is that an and-combination does not *state* a connection, though, if uttered, it *expresses* something, in addition to stating two facts. It expresses at most that the speaker believes there is some connection; it expresses at least that he thinks of the two facts at the same time. But this is a connection among his thoughts, not among the things and facts he thinks about; and things, facts, and their connections (which are a special kind of facts) are what they are, no matter what we think and say about them. The distinction I just made between stating and expressing is clear, I trust. Any gesture, spoken or otherwise, may express something, that is, it may permit one to infer something about the speaker. A grimace or a cry may express pain but it does not state anything, as does the sentence 'I am in pain'. If one neglects this difference, he is again in danger of confusing philosophical analysis and psychology; in this case, the philosophy of language and the psychology of communication. Such reflections are one way of fitting the fundamental insight that some words do not name anything into a web of analytical clarifications. There are others.

Take again 'and' or, rather, its German equivalent 'und', and assume that an English-speaking teacher of German wants to tell his English-speaking pupils what 'und' means. ('Meaning' has philosophical uses; since I use it here commonsensically we need not tarry over them.) Now there are two ways to learn a language. One can learn it, as we have all learned our first one as children, by what language teachers call the direct method. How that works is again a topic in the psychology of language. The second way is by means of another language, which one already understands. Considering this way for a moment, we shall be able to learn something for our purposes. The teacher might say " 'und' means and," just as he could say " 'Katze' means cat." Rather obviously, he could thus translate every German word, at least approximately. The limits of the approximation are the concern of comparative linguistics, not ours. In this respect there is no difference between descriptive and logical words (of German). There is in another. In the case of 'und' the teacher could have said

(1) An 'und'-combination is true if both sentences are true; otherwise it is false.

That is, one can (in English) say what 'und' means without translating it. The case of descriptive words is different. As for 'Katze', the teacher could of course say " 'Katze' means . . . ," where ' . . . ' stands for an (English) definition of (the English) 'cat'. This indicates that we have again run into the distinction between defined and undefined descriptive terms. Consider, then, 'gruen' and 'green', which name the same thing, and which one may plausibly take to be undefined in their respective languages. In this case the teacher, as long as he merely speaks and does not point, which is the direct method, must resort to translation, " 'gruen' means green," " 'schwarz' means black," and so on, descriptive term for descriptive term. There is nothing that corresponds to (1). Moreover, the words of (1) are all either *linguistic,* that is, about language, or logical. The linguistic ones are ' 'und'-combination', 'sentence', and 'true'. For the first two this is obvious, the second being the name of certain kinds of series of words, the first the name of a certain kind of sentence. To be true, finally, is an implicitly relational property of sentences, a sentence being either true or false (not true) according to what the facts are *and according to the rules of the language game.* Clearly, the linguistic words are a class by themselves. Where they fall in our dichotomy between the descriptive and the logical is a nice question and a fundamental one, too, in philosophy proper. I shall therefore say nothing about it. Even so, the difference between (1), which contains only logical and linguistic words, on the one hand, and ' 'gruen' means green', which contains the English name of what 'gruen' names, on the other, is, I think, impressive. What it impresses upon us once more is that the logical words do indeed not name anything—provided, of course, that what I just showed for 'and' can be shown for all of them. Very remarkably, it can be shown. Showing it properly, though, is a very long-winded, very intricate, and very technical affair that belongs again to philosophy proper, more specifically, to the philosophy of logic. This is the place where the philosophical analyst needs the help of mathematical logic perhaps even more than elsewhere. Nor can the analysis be carried out independently. Done technically, it interlocks with the analysis of another dichotomy, that of analytic and synthetic sentences, which we shall presently encounter.

The story of the German teacher can also be used to strengthen our grasp of the analytical method. His English corresponds to the commonsensical way in which the philosophical analyst himself speaks. The German words the language teacher utters correspond to the words of the "improved language," which we may imagine the philosopher "constructs." That is why, if we write down what he says, they appear between single or, as they are also called, *semantical quotes;* for he merely mentions them, that is, he speaks about them and not, by using them, about what they mention. The English words he mentions are philosophical words; either ordinary words philosophically used; or the technical terms of the classical philosophers (I am going out of my way to avoid these in this book); or certain other words, such as 'abstract', which are really philosophical words that have crept into ordinary discourse from early philosophies. His purpose is to restate and to answer the questions that were first discovered by speaking "philosophically." This he does by speaking, quite commonsensically, about his improved language, how it is built, what some of its words name, and so on. So much for what our story tells us positively about the analytical method. Negatively, it helps to call attention to the worst pitfall in all philosophizing. The analyst does of course not speak about German but about "language in general," and in doing so he employs his own language inside and outside of the semantical quotes, if I may so express myself. How easy, then, to overlook the quotes! Yet the moment he overlooks them, he speaks himself "philosophically," falling heir to the notorious evils of this puzzling sort of discourse. A rather effective way to guard against the danger is to use as an improved language or, perhaps better, as the model of one, an artificial sign system, which is not literally a language, of the sort mathematical logicians invent. We shall manage without this tool, though.

What it means for a word to be descriptive I explained, in part, by investigating some that seemed doubtful. The investigation was quite laborious; we were fortunate in that it also afforded us some glimpses at other issues. For the logical words the corresponding investigation will not take long. Yet some things need to be said. Consider the two sentences 'It is raining *but* the sun is shining' and 'He applied for the job *yet* he was not qualified'. Undoubtedly 'but' and 'yet' do not name anything. Yet as they are ordinarily used in sentences such as these, they express that the speaker wishes to say something which he does not literally say or state but which he nevertheless succeeds in conveying. In the first case, had he spoken pedantically, he might have said, 'It is raining and the sun is shining and *this happens rarely in our part of the world';* in the second, 'He applied for the job and he was not qualified and *people do not get jobs for which they are not qualified'* or, perhaps, 'He applied for the job and he was not qualified and *I did not expect that from him'*. Nor does this exhaust what the speaker might have "meant." We usually manage to "understand" because we are familiar with the context. What we understand is in each case stated by the third clause, the clause I underlined, which is, of course, a statement of fact replete with descriptive words. If, however, taking the trouble to speak pedantically, one adds the third clause, then he can as we saw get along without 'but' and 'yet'. 'And' will do. What all that amounts to is this. Ordinary language achieves, at a price, brevity, subtlety, and convenience. The price is ambiguity, the need to rely largely on context, and, most interesting to us, the blurring of such distinctions as that between descriptive and logical words. Only, this does not mean that the distinction itself is blurred. It merely means that one must be aware of the peculiarities of ordinary speech to grasp it firmly. In the case at hand, it seems perfectly reasonable to exclude 'but' and 'yet' from an improved language, just as we excluded 'Hamlet' a while ago. Of course, this is not an "improvement" for the purposes of poetry or of small talk. But I must not be tedious. If what I am driving at is not clear by now then it is either not clear at all or I cannot make it so.

We just got rid of 'but' and 'yet'. Where there were three, 'and', 'but', 'yet', there is now only one, 'and'. The genuinely logical words are in fact rather few and even of these most are expendable, that is, they can be defined in terms of even fewer among them. For instance, 'and', 'not', and 'all' are sufficient. So are 'neither—nor' and 'some'. These are the delights of formal logic with which we must not dally. But there is something in this that fits well as a concluding remark. If the undefinable logical words are surprisingly few, the descriptive ones we cannot define are very numerous, so numerous that an actual enumeration is probably beyond our strength. Just think of all the hues, all the pitches, and all the tastes, not to mention kinds of feelings. Fortunately, one does not need a complete list; we certainly don't need one for our purposes. On the other hand, it is clear that if we grew a new sense or if time became two-dimensional, any such list would become incomplete and we would need a new group of undefined descriptive predicates. We would need no new logical words. The contrast is again striking.

I take it that I have established the distinction between the two kinds of words, logical and descriptive. As with all philosophical distinctions, its real value lies in how it fits with others and in what light it throws on them. Let us see.

TWO KINDS OF SENTENCES

'Olaf is a cat' is true if and only if the thing named 'Olaf' has the character 'cat' names; otherwise it is false. In general, an (indicative) sentence of a properly functioning language is either true or false, depending on the facts. From a sentence itself, even if one understands it, one cannot tell whether it is true or false. Naturally, one must first of all understand it or, as one says, one must know what it means. But this is not enough. Having understood it, one must "look" whether or not what it states is the case. This does not mean that one always must or, for that matter, that one always can look in a literal sense. The truth or falsehood, as the case may be, of a sentence can often be deduced from other sentences about whose truth we have already satisfied ourselves. Eventually such indirect verification or falsification rests on looking, touching, hearing, and so on, in a quite literal sense. For many sentences the direct evidence is not accessible nor is there any way of deducing either their truth or their false-hood from others. 'Caesar's maternal grandfather had a wart on his nose' is very probably of this kind. About such sentences we cannot tell which of the two, true or false, they are. But that causes no philosophical puzzle-ment. The evidence, direct and indirect, for the truth of many other sen-tences remains in a certain sense forever incomplete. All statements of law-fulness are of this sort. A law, as we shall presently see, says something about all instances of a kind. Since one cannot actually "look" at all in-stances, the direct evidence for a law is always incomplete. As to indirect evidence, there is always at least one law among the statements from which another law can be deduced; and the indirect evidence the deduction pro-vides for the latter cannot be better than the direct evidence for the former. In practice there is for the most part more than one such step and the evidences, direct and indirect, overlap and reinforce each other in many ways. This does not affect the principle of the thing. Yet there are many laws about the truth of which we have satisfied ourselves. This is for some a philosophical problem; "induction" is its traditional name. I shall not say anything about induction. I merely mention it on this occasion because I want to say that its problems have not the slightest tendency to throw doubt on the fundamental insight that a sentence is either true or false. The issue in induction is merely how certain we can be of the truth of some sentences. The proper way to handle it is to analyze the highly ambiguous 'certain' and its cognates.

There is still another class of sentences which must be reconciled with what I just called a fundamental insight. Asked about the weather, we sometimes say, without joking, that it is raining and it isn't. Asked whether a certain animal is a wolf or a dog, we may give a similar answer. Lin-guistically, it seems, this amounts to asserting both the truth and falsehood of a sentence. We of course do nothing of the sort. What is here involved is *vagueness* of reference due to the blurred edges of some characters, not the dichotomy true-false. In many cases the blur disappears when our language is made more "precise." Science produces and, when it needs it, strives for this sort of precision. For instance, defining rain at a moment as precipitation above a certain amount during the preceding and subse-quent five minutes as measured by certain instruments will eliminate all doubt in most cases. However, the matter goes rather deep. If 'green' and 'yellow' are among one's basic predicates, then he has no such "scientific" procedure to decide whether, as one says, a certain intermediate hue should be called green or yellow. Even in the rain case we may get bogged down. To see that, one merely has to imagine that the difference between the actual reading and the value which divides rain from not-rain happens to be a fraction of the so-called error of the instrument. There are some genuine problems for analysis in this area. But again, I merely mention them because I want to say that their solution jibes with our fundamental insight. A sentence is either true or false. In this respect there is no difference among (indicative) sentences. There is in another.

Consider the two sentences 'It is raining' and 'Either it is raining or it is not raining'. Both are true; but the first is true only because certain facts are what they are; the second is true whatever the facts may be. Nor is this surprising. The first sentence says something; the second does, in a sense, not say anything. If one knows what the first means, he must still "look" before he can know which of the two, true or false, it is. Whoever understands the second knows without looking that it is true. The first sentence occurs, with the proper specifications of time and place, in weather reports; the second does not. Once it has been pointed out, the difference is again clearly felt, just as is the difference between descriptive and logical words, at least in such clear-cut cases. Sentences of the first kind, those that "say something," are called *synthetic;* the others, *analytic.* A true analytic sentence is also called a *tautology;* a false one, a *contradiction.* The negation of a tautology is a contradiction and conversely. Thus it is not necessary to discuss them both in equal detail; I shall for the most part speak about tautologies. Every sentence is either synthetic or analytic. We have encountered the third of the three fundamental dichotomies, logical-descriptive, true-false, analytic-synthetic.

Take 'It rains or it does not rain' and 'If all cats are carnivorous and Olaf is a cat then Olaf is carnivorous'. They are both true. Notice that I say true, not tautologous, though they are in fact both tautologies. Replace now, in the first, the sentence 'It rains' by 'p'; in the second, the predicates 'cats' and 'carnivorous' by 'A' and 'B', 'Olaf' by 'a'. Consider the two schemata thus obtained, 'p or not-p' and 'If all A are B and a is A then a is B'. Two things stand out. First, each schema contains besides letter symbols only logical words. (In order to make that clear I omitted the article 'a' in 'Olaf is a cat' and wrote 'not-(it rains)' for 'it does not rain'. In an improved language all such vagaries of the various natural languages are of course straightened out.) Second, if each letter symbol is replaced by *any* expression of the proper kind, each occurrence of 'p' by a sentence, each occurrence of 'A' by a predicate, and so on, then the resulting sentence is again true. E.g., 'Peter loves Mary or Peter does not love Mary' and 'If all philosophers are fools and John is a philosopher then John is a fool'. Both these sentences are true. All four, the first pair as well as the second, are tautologies. What makes them tautologies is that their truth depends only on the logical words occurring in them, on how these words are arranged, and, in addition, on the identity or difference, the order and arrangement of the descriptive words, as in the second schema, or of whole component sentences, as in the first. It does not depend on what the descriptive words name, on what the component sentences state, on whether they are true or false. As it has been put, very felicitously I think, in a tautology descriptive words occur only vacuously. This is clarifying. The truth of the sentences that do not say anything depends only on order and arrangement and on those words occurring in them that do not name anything.

To one who is not himself a philosopher what I just said may sound more convincing than it should. I know of no better way to *introduce* the distinction which, I insist, once introduced is clearly felt, than to call the one kind of sentences statements of "fact," the other "nonfactual." A philosopher knows, or should know, that it cannot be *established* so simply in a manner that is dialectically safe. I made my play with 'fact'. But 'fact' is also used philosophically, and some of these uses are so broad that, crudely speaking, everything is a fact and, therefore, every sentence "says something." Thus one would have to explicate the relevant meaning of 'fact' and distinguish it carefully from others. This is indeed part and parcel of the complete analysis of our dichotomy. Only such an analysis can and, I believe, does establish it in a manner that is dialectically safe. Naturally, I shall not undertake it here, contenting myself instead with that partial explication I just gave, which shows how the two dichotomies synthetic-analytic and descriptive-logical jibe with each other. But I shall say a few words about each of several other names by which tautologies are also known. Each of these names suggests a way by which the distinction may be introduced (not established!). Each calls attention to a characteristic feature of the peculiar kind of truth that is called analytic.

Analytic propositions—I use 'sentence', 'statement', and 'proposition' synonymously—are also known as *linguistic truths*. This phrase, too, is suggestive. What suggested it is, probably, that the logical words, since they do not name anything, are, in some sense which is by no means clear, felt to be more "linguistic" than other words. One must not confuse this unclear sense of 'linguistic' with the perfectly clear and different one I explained above.

Another way of referring to analytic statements is to call them *formal truths*. The origin of the phrase is this. Any two sentences which yield the same schema, in the sense in which I just spoke of schemata, may be said to be instances of the same form. With analyticity thus made to depend on "form," one can say that while synthetic sentences state the world's content, analytical ones reflect its form. Another attractive metaphor. Only, one must not forget that without some such specification as I gave 'form' is much too vague to mean anything. Besides, there are other ways of classifying sentences so that any two belonging to the same class may be said to have the same "form."

At the very beginning I said myself that if one understands a tautology one also knows that it is one. This led to the characterization of analyticity as *truth by virtue of meaning*. Again, the formula is attractive; again, it is not very helpful. For one thing, one may wonder whether 'meaning' is not used here philosophically. For another, however it may be used, the formula is not even true. As will soon transpire, every arithmetical statement is analytic, either analytically true or analytically false. So is therefore the formula which states Fermat's famous conjecture; and we know indeed what it means. Do we therefore also know which of the two, true or false, it is? The precise characterization in ordinary English, which in this case includes a lot of nonformalized mathematics, of those sentences of an improved language which are analytic is very technical and rather complicated. We understand it, of course; so we know what it means for a sentence to be analytic. But we also know that it cannot be made to yield a procedure that applies to all sentences and that decides automatically for any one of them whether or not it is analytic. For instance, no machine can answer literally all arithmetical questions. The limits are wide indeed. But they are definite and well understood.

Often tautologies are said to be *necessary* truths, or *certain,* or *indubitable* in that they could *not conceivably* be false. As to 'necessary', I hold with Hume that I do not really know what the word means. Things are what they are. When we do know what we mean, e.g., when we say that something will necessarily happen, we have reference to an impending instance of a well-established law of nature. But this is clearly not what is here involved. The trouble with the other three words is that they refer to kinds or degrees of belief, or to our power of imagination, not to *what* is believed or *what* is or is not being imagined. It is true enough that when we once recognize a proposition as analytic we are very certain of its truth. But this tells something about us rather than about the proposition. Besides, when I see red (and not an intermediate shade), I am just as certain that 'this is red' is true.

I salved my philosophical conscience by pointing at the flaw in each of the formulae I mentioned. I mentioned them because taken together they nevertheless in a nontechnical manner give a fair idea of what the distinction is and why it is fundamental. Most commonly, by the way, analytical truths are spoken of as *logical truths*. The name hints at the crucial part they have in explicating the nature of deductive or logical inference. I turn now to this task.

DEDUCTION

A deductive argument is a pattern of propositions; one or several, called *premisses;* another one, called *conclusion.* The conclusion is said to be deduced or inferred from the premisses, to be implied or entailed by them.

(2)
> Today is Thursday or Friday
> Today is not Friday
> ―――――――――――――――
> Today is Thursday

and

(3)
> All cats are carnivorous
> Olaf is a cat
> ―――――――――――――――
> Olaf is carnivorous

are *valid* arguments. What makes an argument valid? What is the nature of the tie between the premisses of a valid argument and its conclusion? This is the question of logic. The answer will not take us long; for we are now reaping the fruits of our earlier labors.

The validity of an argument depends on its form and only on its form, where form means, as before, the schema that remains after all the descriptive words and, in some cases, whole sentences have been replaced by letter symbols. E.g., (2) and (3) are instances of the forms:

(2′)
$$\frac{p \text{ or } q \quad \text{not-}q}{p}$$
  (3′)
$$\frac{\text{All } A \text{ are } B \quad a \text{ is } A}{a \text{ is } B}.$$

Validity and invalidity must be distinguished from truth and falsehood. A sentence is either true or false. An argument and only an argument is either valid or invalid. Concepts (words, terms) are neither. To speak, as is sometimes done, of concepts as either valid or invalid is merely confusing. What could be meant by calling a concept valid is something entirely different. The name I shall presently choose for this idea is 'significance' (p. 50).

(3a)
> All philosophers are fools
> John is a philosopher
> ―――――――――――――――
> John is a fool

is another instance of (3′) and, therefore, equally valid. Yet its first sentence is probably false; the other two may be either true or false, depending on which John we are speaking of. This shows that what makes an argument valid is neither the truth nor the falsehood of any of its propositions. The connection between truth and validity is this. If all the premisses of a valid argument are true, then its conclusion is true. Instead of saying that in this case the conclusion is true, I might have said that it is necessarily true, using 'necessary' in the same peculiar sense in which it is used when one describes tautologies as necessary truths. In the case of deduction the "necessity" resides, of course, not in the truth of the conclusion—the conclusion of a valid argument may be, but need not be false if at least one of the premises is false—but in the tie between premises and conclusion: *if* the premises of a valid argument are true, then the conclusion is "necessarily" also true. Whence such "certainty"? This is again, in sharper focus, the philosophical problem of logic. The answer lies in the connection between the two notions of validity and tautology. Let

$$P_1$$
$$P_2$$
$$\cdot$$
$$\cdot$$
$$\cdot$$
$$\frac{P_n}{C}$$

be the schema of an argument. It is valid if and only if 'If P_1 and P_2 and . . . and P_n then C' is a tautology. But an instance of the schema 'If . . . then ooooo' is a tautology, that is, it says nothing, if and only if 'ooooo' restates all or part of what ' . . .' states. The conclusion merely makes explicit what is implicit in the premises that "imply" it. Nonmetaphorically the Latin 'explicare' means to unwind, to unravel, to unpack. Just as a tautology "says nothing," so the conclusion of a valid argument does not say "anything new," that is, it says nothing that has not already been said, implicitly, in the premises. This is the key to all the striking peculiarities of deduction. This is why we are so "certain"; this is why the tie is "necessary"; this is why logic is spoken of as "formal" and "nonfactual." The words as well as the ideas are substantially those we encountered when we discussed the nature of tautologies. There is no need to go through all that once more.

Of course, this is not all that can be said about logic. Yet it will suffice for our purposes. The rest can be left to the specialist. The one thing someone who understood what has been said so far may wonder about is the value of logic. If the conclusion says nothing new, why bother? Again, the answer is simple. Our minds are not so constituted that when we grasp what a sentence or a group of sentences says we also know what they imply. To know that, we must "reason" deductively. To lend both conviction and import to this truism, consider the case of geometry. Take Euclidean geometry, with which we are all familiar. Its axioms are few and simple; we all know them after a fashion. Its theorems are many, some very complicated. Yet all theorems, those already "discovered" as well as those nobody has yet thought of, are deductive consequences of the axioms. This is, in fact, what it means for a proposition to be a theorem of Euclidean geometry, just as 'proof' in geometry is but another name for deductive argument. In this respect geometry is the prototype of all scientific theories. It was also historically the first.

Literally there is no truth in a nutshell. Every brief formula pays its price. Nobody can therefore say what science is while his listener stands on one foot. But if I had to choose among the various formulae that have been proposed, I would choose this: The three pillars on which the house of science is built are observation, induction, and deduction. To see what that means, consider our paradigm (3). The second and the third sentence, 'Olaf is a cat' and 'Olaf is carnivorous', are so-called observation statements or statements of individual fact. To find out whether such a statement is true or false one looks and sees.* The first sentence, 'All cats are carnivorous', is a law, a very simple one, to be sure, yet a law; for to be a (synthetic) all-statement or a generality and to be a law is one and the same thing. This law, we may suppose, has been obtained by induction from previous observations of things that are both cats and carnivorous. It does not, of course, follow deductively from the sentences that state those earlier observations. But if we are satisfied that it is true then we can use it to deduce from it and from the statement of an observation we have made ('Olaf is a cat') another observation statement ('Olaf is carnivorous'); and we can do this whether or not we made the latter observation. In practice, the place of the first sentence may be taken by something as complex as virtually the whole of electrodynamics; the place of the second by the detailed description of an intricate machine and of what is done to it, e.g., which switches are thrown on a certain occasion; the place of the third by a description of what happens on this occasion. Such complexity does not affect the principle of the thing. As far as it goes, our illustration is an accurate account of the respective roles observation, induction, and deduction play in science. What it does not illustrate is the role of defined concepts on the one hand and the nature of theory on the other. To definition an entire section of this chapter will be devoted. The nature of scientific theory is, in a sense, the main topic of this book; it will occupy us from the second chapter on. But we are ready for a first glimpse even now.

If there has to be a formula again, one might say that a theory is a group of laws deductively connected. More accurately, a theory is a group of laws, usually rather few, from which others, usually a larger number, have actually been deduced and from which one expects to deduce still further ones. The laws that serve as the premisses of these deductions are called the *axioms* of the theory; those which appear as conclusions are called its

* See, however, p. 25.

theorems. Given a group of laws, there is sometimes more than one way of selecting a subgroup so that all others in the group follow deductively from those of the subgroup. This shows that to call a law either an axiom or a theorem is not to say anything about the law itself; it merely says something about its position in a theory. The descriptive words that occur in the propositions of a theory may be called its vocabulary. The fundamental principle that a descriptive term not referring to what we are directly acquainted with must be defined, applies to the vocabulary of a theory as it does to all descriptive words. Only, a theory need not always pay explicit attention to all these definitions. It does and must to some. More often than not, a theory is, as it were, a partial language all by itself, that is, the words of its vocabulary fall into two classes so that each of the one, usually the larger, can be defined in terms of the other, usually the smaller, *alone*. The latter may then be said to be the basic or undefined vocabulary of the theory. To the definitions of the former the theory must pay attention. To grasp this firmly, assume that, as is often the case, all the descriptive words in the axioms of a theory belong to its basic vocabulary. To derive from them a law that contains a nonbasic term one must obviously use its definition. If, for instance, the axioms of Euclidean geometry do not contain 'circle', one must use its definition in order to deduce from them a theorem about circles. Technically, such definitions become additional premisses of the deduction. But all definitions are, as we shall presently see, analytic; and an analytic proposition, not saying anything, is not materially an "additional" premiss.

As it stands, this explication of 'theory' covers a bit too much. As the word is used in any well-developed science, to be a theory a group of laws must have a certain *scope*. This is not a very precise notion; nor would there be any point in trying to make it precise. Roughly, one might say that a theory should cover a certain range of phenomena and that its laws should be rather different from each other. However, notions that are by their very nature not precise should be illustrated rather than, literally, explicated. Let us call a lever any rigid body supported at one point on which two forces act so that the point of support does not shift. Call the two forces p_1 and p_2, the distances of their lines of attack from O, the point of support, d_1 and d_2 (Fig. 1). The condition of equilibrium is $p_1 d_1 = p_2 d_2$.

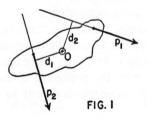

FIG. I

(I omit for simplicity's sake the specification of directions.) This is the "general" law of the lever. If the lever is a straight rod and the force lines are parallel, one has $d_1 : d_2 = l_1 : l_2$; in words, the distances are proportional to the lengths of the so-called "arms" of such a lever (Fig. 2). This

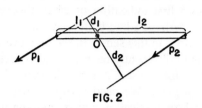

FIG. 2

yields $p_1 l_1 = p_2 l_2$ as the condition of equilibrium in this case. We have, by "specializing" the "general" law, deduced another. Specializing this one further, one easily derives a third: if the two arms of a (rod) lever are equal, then the two (parallel) forces must be equal if there is to be equilibrium. In fact, we could derive an infinite number of such laws, one for each ratio of the lengths of the arms. Literally, they are all different laws. Literally, what we have here is therefore a theory. Its one axiom is the "general" law of the lever; its theorems are the various specializations of this law. Yet physicists would hardly call it a theory, because it lacks scope. Newton's theory of gravitation, which contains among other things the laws of planetary motion, the laws of freely falling bodies, and the laws of the tides, has scope. This shows what it means to say that a "theory," in order to really be one or to be worthy of the name, must have "scope."

Which feature or features of a theory account for its scope or power is an interesting problem in analysis. I shall deal with the most decisive of these features, the occurrence of so-called composition rules among the axioms, in the third chapter at some length. Most theories of some scope do, in fact, also have another feature, which I may just as well mention now. The distinction I intend by speaking once of a feature *accounting* for a theory's scope, once of a feature most such theories *possess,* should be clear. In the former case the analyst explains something; in the latter he merely points at a very general fact. To state such facts articulately belongs indeed to his task. This is part of what is meant by those who insist that philosophy is merely a peculiar sort of description of the world and the philosophy of science, therefore, merely such a description of science. The feature in question, the one which most powerful theories do in fact possess, is that their basic vocabulary is, in terms of what we are directly acquainted with, rather highly defined. 'Highly defined' is neither a very pretty nor a very clear phrase. What I am trying to say is that the basic vocabulary of most such theories is, in several meanings of that ambiguous word, rather abstract. But I dislike 'abstract' even more than 'highly defined'. At this point one who understands completely what has been said so far but knows nothing else may again wonder. Euclidean geometry is a theory of very wide scope; yet its basic vocabulary refers to what we are directly acquainted with. Geometry is the only such theory I can think of. And it is exceptional in still another respect. Time is not mentioned in it.

This will suffice as a first indication of what 'theory' means in a well-developed science. Or perhaps I had better say that a science is called well developed if it has theories in this sense. In the less well-developed behavior sciences the word has until recently been used with several different meanings. Occasionally it is still so used. A brief glossary of these meanings will therefore not be out of place. We need hardly bother with the broadest of all uses of 'theory' and 'theoretical' in which anything not relevant to one's immediate practical concerns becomes theory. But consider the following case. When the so-called illusions aroused the interest of the psychologists, all sorts of "theories" were expounded to explain them. One of these, probably suggested by the diagram Mueller-Lyer has made so familiar (Fig. 3), was that length estimates tend toward the corresponding dimension of

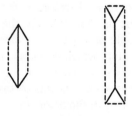

FIG. 3

the smallest convex figure in which the design whose length is being estimated can be inscribed. What these "theorists" proposed is much better called a law. It is in fact a rather isolated law without, at least at that time, any deductive connection with others; and, even as laws go, of very narrow scope. Nor, for that matter, has it ever been well established. This leads to another usage. Any conjecture as yet not well established, either of law or even of individual fact, is sometimes called a theory. With respect to individual facts, this is the sense in which those master minds whose exploits so fascinate us in a certain kind of fiction propound theories about where the body is buried and what weapon was used to dispatch it. Less fancifully, a clinician may have a "theory" that a certain event, about which his patient either can't or won't tell, took place in his life. Similarly, historians have "theories" about what happened in the past. With respect to both individual facts and laws as yet not established, this meaning of 'theory' is synonymous with one meaning of 'hypothesis'. (Nor does it improve matters that, using 'hypothesis' philosophically, some call any law or any theory, no matter how well established, hypothetical merely because of the ubiquitous hazards of induction. But I am dealing with the ambiguities of 'theory', not with those of 'hypothesis'.) Another use of 'theory' is even more pretentious. Sometimes a "theory" is not even a guess at a law but merely a conjecture as to which variables may occur in the laws of a certain area. Freud's teachings, for instance, were called a theory even at a time when all they amounted to was, in sober parlance, a conjecture about the role of sexual factors in the field of personality.

Psychologists who write about the philosophy of their field are often quite struck by ideas which happen to be discussed in philosophy proper or in the philosophy of physics, hoping, somewhat naively, that here at last is the magic word, the key to the closed gate. Usually the enthusiasm dies quickly, only to be replaced by another. It is not my intention to make this book a critical record of such passing fancies of the present and the recent past. Some, though, deserve mention, partly because their impact was rather great, partly because the ideas themselves are important, though not necessarily within the philosophy of psychology. *Axiomatization* and *formalization* are two such ideas. The natural place to take them up is in a discussion of deduction and, therefore, of theory.

A scientific theory consists of (1) axioms, (2) theorems, (3) the proofs of these theorems, and (4) definitions. Assume now that in the exposition of a theory all descriptive words have been replaced by letter symbols; in an exposition of geometry, for instance, every occurrence of 'point' by 'P_1', every occurrence of 'straight line' by 'P_2' and so on. Or assume that all the descriptive words, in the case of geometry all geometrical words, have been replaced by their equivalents in a language we do not understand, say, Tamil. If we are presented with the exposition of a theory that has been altered in this manner, we do not know, though we might in some cases conceivably guess, what it is the theory of. Nor can we form an opinion as to whether any of the (synthetic) sentences (1) and (2) are true; obviously not, since we do not know what the descriptive words occurring in them name. More precisely, the doctored account does not contain any "descriptive words," just as its "sentences" are merely schemata and no longer really sentences. Yet from this doctored account of a theory we could check everything that pertains to deduction and definition in the theory itself. We could even add similarly doctored "theorems," "proofs," and "definitions" of our own. This is the heart of the matter. One is almost tempted to say, this is all there is to it. As a science develops, a store of laws and concepts accumulates together with an awareness of some connections, deductive among the laws, definitional among the concepts. At a certain point in the development it pays to arrange this material into a theory. The advantages are of two kinds. Positively, one will then know, accurately and as one could not possibly know otherwise, what depends upon what and how and why. Also, a theory guides the search for new laws and for new significant definitions. Of this I shall speak later. Negatively, one's attention will be drawn to what has been either overlooked or taken for granted, either by way of premisses or by way of definitions. Thus past errors and ambiguities or simply gaps may be discovered; future ones may be avoided. Euclid was the first who did this sort of thing when he *axiomatized* the geometrical knowledge of his time. If one wants to take all possible precautions that nothing has been overlooked or taken for granted so that the deductive structure is completely tight, one may sometimes with profit proceed formally or *formalize* the theory by replacing all descriptive words with letter symbols. This Euclid did not do; and he did, in fact, overlook a few things. The first axiomatization of Euclidean geometry that stands up under modern logical criticism came as late as 1899. It is due to Hilbert.

Obviously axiomatization or even formalization is not the magic key. If enough material has accumulated, one will axiomatize it as a matter of course and probably reap the benefits that attend the possession of an articulate theory of some scope. Whether or not psychology has as yet reached this stage is a matter of judgment. Axiomatization or even formalization as such does not add anything to the scope of what is being axiomatized. In my opinion some psychologists have been much too self-conscious about axiomatization. Occasionally the "rigor" is carried to the extreme of wanting to supplant ordinary English by the apparatus of formal logic. The fruitfulness of this advice at the present stage of knowledge still remains to be demonstrated. (One of the attendant naiveties is the confusion between formalization and quantification, that is, the use of numbers. Yet physics and even mathematics itself are, with rare exceptions, pursued in ordinary English.) On the other hand, some of the most successful theorists in psychology, those making the most elaborate deductions now extant and inventing the most significant concepts now available, are among the least self-conscious. One more thing must be said, though. Even behaviorism has not completely disposed of anthropomorphism in psychology. We are all sometimes "frustrated"; we are in certain states which we describe, when we speak commonsensically and use our words nontechnically, as states of "frustration." Assume that we know, in the ordinary commonsensical way of knowing in which we all know or believe we know a few things about ourselves and others, that when we are "frustrated" we are also "aggressive." Assume next that a behaviorist has defined the two technical terms 'frustration' and 'aggression' in the most unimpeachably operational and objective manner. (I am not really using these two words 'operational' and 'objective'; I am merely parading them.) Even such a one may overlook that to be valid his reasoning requires a premiss such as, say, 'frustration produces aggression'. A physicist handling such terms as 'paramagnetic' and 'polarized' is less likely to make this sort of mistake. For 'para-magnetic' and 'polarized' have no nonscientific use and we ourselves are never in paramagnetic or polarized states or, if we are, we do not know it as we sometimes know ourselves to be frustrated and aggressive. The fascination with axiomatization and formalization has, I believe, greatly reduced the danger of this subtler form of anthropomorphism in psychology. For the rest, the fuss was about nothing. In the philosophy of science the two notions of axiomatization and formalization appear in the analysis of the nature of scientific theories in general; in the analysis of the problems peculiar to the philosophy of psychology they are of no specific use. The idea of formalization has had an interesting development in philosophy proper. I shall mention it briefly in order to add further to our grasp of the analytical method.

Formalization has been put to an important use in solving the problems raised by the so-called elementary particles of physics. It will be remembered that I once called 'electron' a special case (p. 18). Instead of singling out electrons, I could have mentioned the recent positron or the old-fashioned atoms and molecules of the kinetic theory of, say, 1890. The fundamental question is the same for all of them. How does, say, 'atom' get into a language that conforms to the Principle of Acquaintance? There are two kinds of answer. The one (a) uses the idea of formalization; the other (b) introduces the crucial terms, like all other "abstract" concepts, by definition.

(a) The so-called mechanical model is conceived as a language or "calculus" C in itself, which is interpreted (tied to the language L which we speak and understand) by a peculiar set of "coordination rules." Their peculiarity is that not all terms and sentences of C are or need be "translatable" and, therefore, given the coordination rules, open to experimental check. For instance, a certain statement about an average speed in C translates into an L-statement about the temperature of a gas. But there is no L-statement (or there need not be, or there is none at a certain state of the theory) that corresponds to a C-statement about the speed of an individual particle. Consequently, if (some of) the undefined descriptive terms of C were added to the vocabulary of L, they would not be eliminable. All defined terms are eliminable; this is part of what it means to be a defined term. The coordination rules are therefore not technically definitions of the undefined descriptive terms of C and the procedure of introducing "abstract" concepts in this manner is *sui generis*. Sometimes concepts so introduced are said to name "hypothetical" or "theoretical" entities. This is another, very specialized use of the two words (see p. 35).

(b) The notion of a sphere of a size one can touch and which moves in orbits can be formulated in L. Reducing it in scale merely adds an arithmetical idea. The crucial terms are therefore literally definable. What is, upon (a), a correspondence between a statement of L and one of C, say, in the case of the temperature of a gas, thus becomes, upon (b), simply a statement of L.

Misusing words by using them philosophically, one can from (a) arrive at the "philosophical" doctrine that the particles are merely "fictions," that they are not "real" or do not "exist." Similarly, (b) may lead to the opposite doctrine. Things are not improved if these two "positions" are confused with two other ones in philosophy proper with which they have really nothing to do. Yet the "fictionalists" buttressed their arguments with those of the "phenomenalists," while the "particle realists" sought aid and comfort from the "realists" (and sometimes vice versa). But the situation is even more dialectical than that.

As experimentation progressed, the particle became more and more "concrete." We "see" a flash on a screen and say that a particle has passed through a slit in the apparatus. The particle realist would like to say that by now we actually "see" the particle. Presumably this embarrasses the fictionalist. I see no cause for embarrassment. We do not always say that a particle is passing through a slit when we see a flash. Thus the statement about the latter is in need of analysis. Fully expanded, it becomes a statement not only about the flash but also about the apparatus and what is being done to it. A statement about the passage of a physical object need not and cannot be so expanded. In this sense we shall of course never actually "see" particles.

As theory developed, particles no longer moved in orbits, thus losing one of the fundamental characteristics of physical objects. Presumably this embarrasses the realist. It does embarrass the particle realist; for, in a sense, but, as closer analysis reveals, only in a sense, the particle has bowed out of physical theory (see p. 124). The philosophical realist, however, is not necessarily committed to the belief that "reality" is in any respect like what we "see." So he is not embarrassed.

Some people seem to believe that mental contents are like particles in that certain philosophical questions that can be asked about them cannot be answered without resorting to formalization (alternative (a) above). These ideas are so confused that I shall not bother either to state or to refute what they could possibly mean.

One formalizes a scientific theory by replacing its descriptive words with "marks on paper." The logical words, which remain, are the only ones we "understand." What happens if they, too, are replaced by marks? One obvious consequence is that one can no longer check the deductions. All one could undertake, quite literally and not just metaphorically, is a study in geometrical design. Let us relate this idea to one we encountered before. The philosophical analyst distinguishes between the language he actually speaks in a studiedly commonsensical fashion, say, English, and the "improved language," which he imagines he "constructs." (Actually, he constructs merely its schema or outline.) The most radical way to safeguard the distinction is to imagine that he performs his task in three successive steps. (This time I speak of imagining because practically he has, of course, always his goal in mind.) His first step is a job in geometrical design. He selects certain kinds of shapes as the prospective "words," certain kinds of series of such shapes as the prospective "sentences," and so on. Notice that I said prospective; for by themselves marks on paper are just marks on paper. This first step is called *syntactical;* from it the analytical method is also known as the syntactical or formal method. In the second step the analyst interprets this schema, e.g., by translating certain kinds of shapes, say, the prospective "undefined descriptive terms," as in: 'gruen' means green. In the third step he uses the interpreted schema or, as I called it, the improved language, to investigate the philosophical problems (which he himself merely mentions). It turns out that the core of both questions and answers hinges upon the syntax and the interpretation of the improved language. Thus it can be stated in a commonsensical manner.

By proceeding strictly formally or syntactically the analyst not only prevents himself from speaking "philosophically" (p. 19); he also makes sure that nothing is "overlooked" or "taken for granted." I use the same words as before in the case of geometry because the advantage is of the same kind. (Otherwise, we see, 'formalization' in science and its philosophy does not mean what it means in logic and philosophy proper. In the former only the descriptive words are replaced by "meaningless marks on paper.") But this is not the main reason for sometimes insisting on a strictly syntactical approach. The main reason is that the analysis of *some* philosophical problems (as well as a completely foolproof statement of the method itself) depends on a strictly syntactical conception of the improved language. For instance, and I have hinted at this before, if one wants to analyze completely the two dichotomies logical-descriptive and analytic-synthetic, one must start by considering all words (of the improved language) as mere marks on paper. Fortunately this is not so for *all* philosophical problems. At least, one can say a good deal about many of them without subjecting either one's self or one's readers to all the rigors of syntax. There is still another dimension of freedom in this improved-language game.

The philosophical problems, both questions and answers, are all more or less closely and directly connected with each other. Ideally one must therefore try to solve them all—simultaneously, as it were—if one wants to solve any. In our method this idea reflects itself in the search for an *ideal language*. An ideal language is an improved language syntactically constructed that fulfills two conditions. (1) Anything one might want to say, provided one does not use words "philosophically," can in principle be stated in it. (2) It is an adequate tool for the analysis of all philosophical problems in what I just called the third step of the method. Practically, we often limit ourselves to some problems, say, for instance, those of the philosophy of physics. Using the analytical method, we shall again construct an improved language. This language or, more precisely, this schema of one, call it P, will not necessarily be the ideal language; for it need not fulfill (1) and (2). Two weaker criteria suffice. (1′) Physics can, in principle, be stated in P. (2′) P is an adequate tool for the analysis of all problems in the philosophy of physics. Apart from technicalities which, metaphorically speaking, belong into small print and which I just literally

put there, it is virtually noncontroversial that both (1′) and (2′) are fulfilled by *a language, otherwise properly improved, whose undefined descriptive terms name physical objects and some of those properties of and relations among them with which we are, commonsensically speaking, directly
acquainted*. The italicized phrase is almost prohibitively long; casting about
for a shorter one to replace it, one is tempted to call such a schema
"realistic." The word is philosophical; the price of convenience is therefore a host of unwelcome associations. Yet I shall sometimes use it, though
never without surrounding it by quotes in order to discourage those associations. In physics, then, a "realistic" language fulfills both (1′) and (2′).
Let us steal a first glance at the situation in psychology. Much of the confusion there stems from the failure to distinguish between the two criteria.
A language fulfills (1″) if and only if the science of psychology can, in
principle, be stated in it; it fulfills (2″) if and only if it is an adequate
tool for the analysis of all philosophical questions that can be asked about
the science of psychology. The point is that a language may fulfill (1″)
without fulfilling (2″). Confused "behaviorists" contend that *the proper
language of psychology* is "realistic." Their confused opponents insist that
it is "phenomenalistic." 'Phenomenalistic' is another philosophical word,
not safely used without quotes. It is nonetheless a convenient short name
for the kind of schema whose undefined descriptive terms refer to mental
things, that is, the one sort of thing with which we are directly acquainted—
according to the "phenomenalists," who do not use the phrase 'being
directly acquainted' commonsensically. The ideal language, by the way,
is "phenomenalistic." The confusion that bedevils both the "behaviorists"
and the "antibehaviorists" hides behind the phrase I italicized, *the proper
language of psychology*. The trouble with it is that it obscures the distinction between the two criteria. To show that the "realistic" language fulfills
(1″), one need not, as the confused behaviorists do, argue that it also
fulfills (2″). The "phenomenalistic" language fulfills both (1″) and (2″).
To show this, one need not, as the confused antibehaviorists do, argue that
the realistic language does not fulfill (1″).

This is, of course, one of the major issues which I must discuss. I shall
deal with it at considerable length in Volume Two. What I said now is
merely a hint, tantalizing perhaps and, at best, intriguing. I threw out this
hint in order to reassure the reader that what I am discussing now will be
needed later. But he must be patient. Whatever I could possibly achieve
would be spoiled by skipping or even speeding beyond reason. It will in
fact be necessary to devote one more section, the next, to questions that
are mostly logical and linguistic and that belong therefore more nearly to
philosophy proper. In this I shall, as throughout this book, assume that the
improved language about which I speak is "realistic." It is clear by now, I
trust, that in doing this I am not stacking the cards. Many things can be

learned from either schema. With respect to logic there is no difference whatsoever between the two; naturally not, since the only difference between them lies in the interpretation of the undefined descriptive terms.

'SOME' AND 'EXISTS'

Consider 'Peter is blond' and 'Peter strawberries nor'. The first is a sentence. The second is not; it is, as one says, a nonsensical string of words. To ask whether it is true or, even, what it states (means) would be futile. As we ordinarily speak, we do not find it difficult to distinguish between nonsense and a sentence, however false, queer, or foolish the latter may be, such as, say, 'The moon is made of green cheese'. Three adjectives, for instance, or three nouns do not make a sentence. 'Adjective' and 'noun', we notice, are grammatical terms. Generally, what is not grammatically correct, in the ordinary sense of 'grammar', is certainly nonsense. If the grammatical error is relatively slight, we may guess what is meant; but this is beside the point. About some grammatically correct sentences, one may wonder, though. Take Russell's illustration, 'Quadruplicity drinks procrastination'. Is it, like 'The moon is made of green cheese', a sentence; or is it, like 'Peter strawberries nor', nonsense? One may be inclined to call it nonsense, since we know that "abstractions" do not and cannot "possibly" drink other abstractions. But, then, what is an abstraction; and what does it mean for a state of affairs to be possible? We have landed with both feet in philosophy. Ordinarily one relies on both context and grammar. In some cases context lets us down and ordinary grammar, we discover, does not provide a set of rules sufficiently systematic to cover them. The first step in "improving" a language is to develop such rules. This is the fundamental part of syntax which is, therefore, sometimes also called logical grammar. 'Ideal grammar' would perhaps express the idea more adequately.

Let us borrow from ordinary grammar and begin with *simple clauses,* calling a simple clause a sentence from which no word can be omitted without its becoming nonsense. 'Peter is blond and it is raining' is not a simple clause, since what remains when either the first four or the last four words are omitted is still a sentence. Some simple clauses contain no logical words. They are, in a sense, the simplest of all and are, therefore, called *atomic sentences.* In ordinary language the distinction between logical and descriptive words is, as we saw, sometimes blurred. Yet, as ordinary language goes, the 'is' in 'Peter is blond' is indubitably logical. To grasp that clearly, one merely has to consider that it is expendable. 'Peter blond' or, in general, a one-term predicate and its subject put together would do. Some languages very closely related to ours, such as Russian, actually omit this 'is'. So does every improved language. Similarly, a two-term predicate together with two subjects, a three-term predicate together with three subjects, and so on, are atomic sentences. In an improved language—I shall from now on often suppress this self-evident qualification—all atomic sentences are of this form—let us call it the subject-predicate form. Compared with our natural languages, the simplification is sweeping as it is. It becomes even more so in view of the following. Every sentence can be made from atomic sentences by the successive application of two operations. (1) Sentences can be compounded from others by the so-called *connectives*. These are logical words that are put between or, in the case of 'not', before sentences. E.g., 'if *p* and *q* then not-*r*' is the schema of a sentence compounded from three others by means of 'not', 'and', and 'if-then'. (2) The ideas expressed by the two logical words 'all' and 'some' can be introduced in either the subject places or the predicate places of any sentence. For the subject place of an atomic sentence, say, 'Peter is blond', this yields 'Everything is blond' (which is false) and 'Something is blond' (which is true). These, by the way, are simple clauses that are not atomic since they contain the logical words 'everything (all)' and 'something (some)', which, unlike 'is', are not expendable. I shall say no more about connectives. To 'all' and 'some', particularly to 'some', I shall attend presently.

The notion of a subject which I just used is not that of a kind of word but, rather, that of a kind of position a word may have in a sentence. Thus one might have expected that I would call 'Peter' a proper name instead of calling it a subject, since I set out to characterize sentences syntactically, that is, by specifying the kinds of words that go together to make one. Yet I could not have used 'proper name'; for, as it turns out, the explication of 'proper name' itself is in terms of 'subject' and 'predicate'. Use 'this' for a "proper name" and consider the two sentences 'this is green' and 'green is a color'. In the first, 'green', which is a predicate, stands in the predicate place; in the second, it stands in the subject place. Some predicates, we see, are in some sentences in the predicate place, in some others in the subject place. This is our clue for the explication of 'proper name'. A proper name is an undefined descriptive term that always stands in the subject place, never in the predicate place. It will be remembered that I promised such a grammatical explication of 'proper name' (p. 13).

Notice the distinction I just made between *predicate* and *predicate place*. As I introduced and used it, 'predicate' refers indeed to a kind of word, namely, words that name characters. This is of course not a purely syntactical definition. But then, neither is this a completely rigorous and systematic exposition. It is merely a preparation for something else.

The fact that in ordinary language predicates occur in both places is at the root of a problem every improved language must face. Surely, we do not want to call 'green is blue' or, more precisely, what corresponds to it in an improved language, a sentence. It ought to be nonsense. On the other hand, 'green is (a) color' ought to be a sentence. It is even true. (The 'is' in the true sentence 'green is green' is another 'is', which, though definable by other logical words, is not expendable as is the subject-predicate 'is'. It signifies "identity.") There are two alternatives. One can try to construct the improved language so that there are only two kinds of descriptive words, subjects which stand in the subject place and predicates which stand in the predicate place. This so restricts the expressive possibilities of the schema that it can for some problems no longer serve as an improved language. Or, and this is the second alternative, one must introduce a syntactical distinction among predicates. This is done in Russell's celebrated *theory of logical types*. There are also other "logical" devices which achieve the same goal. Accordingly, they amount essentially to the same thing. Or, rather, we can leave the choice among them, if there is one, to philosophy proper. I shall continue to speak quite naively of predicates, even though one cannot escape these issues either in the philosophy of mathematics or if one proceeds formally in the construction of the improved language. But I have said several times already that I shall not do that.

'Exist' is essentially a philosophical word; its nonphilosophical or ordinary uses are all expendable; the burden can, as we shall presently convince ourselves, be carried by the logical 'some'. But let me first demonstrate the value of what has been said so far. Some insist that only physical objects exist (1a); or only physical objects and some of their characters (1b). Others maintain that only mental objects exist, sense data, percepts, feelings, and so on (2a); or only mental objects and some of their characters, such as sensory and feeling qualities (2b). Still others propound the existence of both mental and physical objects. Surely, they all speak philosophically. Surely, we must try to get to the bottom of these philosophical statements. If we want to find out what they could possibly mean, or, as I put it a while ago, discover their core, we must analyze them by our method. Now I have mentioned before that the dialectic of what "exists" or is "real," that is, the philosophical uses of 'exist', is not unconnected with such uses of 'name' and 'naming' (p. 15). I pointed out, for instance, that those who want only "concrete" objects to exist, refuse to say that character words "name" anything (whether or not the characters named are exemplified). This is our clue. It appears that what some philosophers mean can be quite commonsensically stated as follows; what "exists" is what is named by a proper name. These are the positions (1a) and (2a). What some others mean is similarly explicated by: what "exists" is what is named by an undefined descriptive term, either proper name or predicate. These are the positions (1b) and (2b). As I have also indicated before, those who choose variant (a) of either (1) or (2) are probably guided by the metaphor of pointing. For them, to exist or to be real, to be named by a proper name, and to be point-at-able are one and the same thing. What they defend is of course not a statement of fact but a way of using words philosophically. If one had to choose among the possible philosophical meanings of 'exist', I would say that variant (b) is more reasonable. But I shall say no more about this disagreement among philosophers and turn instead to the alternatives (1) and (2), considering, for brevity's sake, only their variants (a). As I explicated it, 'proper name' is a strictly syntactical notion. What a proper name names still depends on the interpretation of the schema. The proper names of a "realistic" language name physical objects. The proper names of a "phenomenalistic" language name mental things. Which, then, are the real proper names? To us this question makes no sense. Those, however, who are less self-conscious about language have quite definite notions about what ought to be named by proper names. The hidden or unconscious grammar, if I may so put it, is the same as before. The idea expressed by means of it is that what exists or is real or, if you please, what really exists is what is simple, a sort of element or building stone that cannot be taken apart or "analyzed." This is, of course, a nonphilosophical meaning of 'analysis'. A psychological version of it dominates, as we shall see in Volume Three, virtually half of the history of modern psychology. Be that as it may, we have come across another ingredient of these confused philosophical notions of "existence" or "reality." Only what is simple exists. All other "things" are merely combinations of the building stones; and combinations as such do not "exist." Whatever the merits of this idea, its explication by our method is rather obvious. Remember that the ideal language is the one in which everything nonphilosophical can be stated and by means of which all philosophical problems can be analyzed. Now an undefined term of this language need not and, in a certain sense, cannot be further "analyzed." This is the cue. To be "simple" means to be named by an undefined descriptive term of the ideal language. From where we stand this of course does not show what things ought to be named by proper names. It merely shows that our explications ought to be amended. Variant (a), for instance, ought to read: what exists is what is named by a proper name of the ideal language. Similarly for (b). What is at issue between (1) and (2) is better not stated in terms of "existence." One issue, we saw, is what we are directly acquainted with. Another, as we now see, is what is simple.

Such explications of the philosophical uses of 'exist' all belong to the analyst's own commonsensical language, not to the improved language from which he expurgates them. The attempt to make such explications in the latter is the predicament of all preanalytical philosophy. Its obscurity stems from failure to distinguish between the two languages or, less technically, between discourse on the one hand and discourse about discourse (and what it is about) on the other. In the case at hand, the attempt is not only obscure but also peculiarly futile. Consider those who say, however obscurely, that what "exists" is what is named by a proper name and remember Hamlet and the blind man whose improved language could not contain an undefined 'green' (p. 14). Since Hamlet does not "exist," there is no 'Hamlet' in an improved language; conversely, if Peter did not "exist," there would be no 'Peter' in it. What the hapless philosopher tries to say *shows itself* in an improved language by the occurrence of a proper name (or, variant (b), either a proper name or an undefined predicate). 'Peter exists', if 'Peter' be a proper name, is redundant at best. This is one of Russell's fundamental insights.

So much for the negative part of the analysis of the philosophical uses of 'exist'. Positively, it remains to be shown that whenever 'exist' is used to say something which is neither philosophical nor redundant it can be replaced by 'some', which is a logical word and not a verb; so that we are not tempted to say that a thing "somes" any more than that it "ands" or "alls." But first for a concluding remark on proper names.

The pressing problems of the analysis of logic (deduction, definition, theory) require that the improved language be of the subject-predicate form, that is, that an atomic sentence consist of a predicate, its subject or subjects, and nothing else. It is worth noticing, then, that what I have so far called a "realistic" language could not possibly be of this form. Use 'this' for the name of a lobster. While the animal is alive, 'This is green' is true; after it has been boiled, the sentence is false. Similarly for relations. 'Peter is to the left of John' is true when they are in certain positions; it is false after they have changed places. This contradicts the fundamental insight that no sentence is both true and false. To safeguard it, an atomic sentence of a "realistic" schema must in addition to a predicate and its subject or subjects contain a temporal determination, which destroys the desired syntactical form. The things named by the proper names of a "phenomenalistic" language are "momentary"; they are not, as one says, continuants (in time). Such a language therefore does not encounter this particular difficulty. To overcome it in a "realistic" schema, its proper names must be made to name not physical objects but thin temporal slices of their history. This shows that a schema whose proper names refer to physical objects cannot be the ideal language. Nor is this surprising. A little reflection convinces one that the interdependent notions of change and physical identity could not possibly be analyzed by means of an improved language whose proper names name physical objects. Yet these notions are in need of analysis; for we say 'this is the man I saw yesterday' although what we see today is different in some respects from what we saw yesterday and although, even if it is not, we do not have the same percept we had yesterday. On the other hand, I have not proved that after it has been amended as I just suggested, a "realistic" language cannot be the ideal language. As it happens, it is not, though it will do for many purposes. I shall even continue to speak, inaccurately, as if the proper names of a "realistic" language named physical objects. For my purposes this inaccuracy will do no harm. I merely wanted to mention the point, partly to salve my philosophical conscience, partly to sharpen the notion of a proper name.

'Some' and 'all' are best treated together since each of the two is easily defined in terms of the other: 'not-some-not' can stand for 'all', 'not-all-not' can stand for 'some'. E.g., 'Not all cats are not black' means the same as 'Some cats are black'. Thus one of the two, we can make our choice, is expendable. This is of some interest in itself since there is, at least in languages similar to ours, no verb connected with 'all' the way 'exist' is connected with 'some'. To see this connection, consider the three sentences (1) 'Some cats are black', (2) 'There are black cats', (3) 'Black cats exist'. They all say the same thing. (1) contains the lowly 'some'; (3) contains the seductive verb. (2) is best suited for our purposes. Sometimes it pays to rewrite it so that it reads (4) 'There is at least one thing (there are things) such that it is a cat and it is black' or, even, (4') 'There is an x: x is a cat and x is black'. (4) and (4') force upon our attention that what is stated is the "existence" (philosophical use!) not of a character but of an instance of one. Whoever sees that clearly will eventually see through the spurious uses of 'exist'.

Take an *undefined* predicate, say, 'green' and form the some-sentence 'There is an x: x is green'. Well-formed and even true as it is, it is nevertheless peculiar. If we built and used our language according to our principles, then we know by this token alone that the sentence is true. For the Principle of Acquaintance (p. 15), we remember, requires that an undefined predicate occur in an improved language only if the user is directly acquainted with an instance of it; hence it must have an instance; and this is exactly what our sentence says. In this sense it is redundant. But assume now that we have seen black objects and that we have seen cats but that we have never seen a black cat. If we know nothing else, then we do not know whether or not (4') is true. If we know some other things, then we may deduce it from indirect evidence; otherwise we must wait for future experience. This shows that (4') is not redundant. All nonredundant uses of 'some' and, therefore, of 'exist', e.g., 'Mermaids do not exist' are of this kind. They all involve *defined* predicates.

Let us throw a quick glance at the corresponding situation for 'all'. Take 'Everything is green', or, preferably, 'For every x: x is green'. Significant though it is in a sense, it is false, and so are all all-sentences formed with one predicate, whether defined or undefined. We know no (descriptive) character possessed by everything. All practically important uses of 'all' occur in compound sentences. Take, for instance, 'For every x: if x is A then x is B'. This is but another way of saying 'All A are B'; it is the way in which generality is expressed in a logically improved language.

I mentioned earlier (p. 15) that definite descriptions would have to be transcribed in an improved language. The idea of the transcription depends on 'some' and on "identity." Identity is a logical relational character possessed by everything. Everything is identical with itself and with nothing else. Outside of mathematics (the 'is' or '=' in '2 + 2 = 4' signifies identity) the usefulness of stating identities is therefore rather limited. Yet there are uses; e.g., in 'The husband of Mary is the mayor of the town'; for to say that two definite descriptions are of the "same" thing conveys information. Taking his cue from an idea of Leibniz, Russell has shown that identity ('=') is a defined logical relation word. Using it one can write

(1)   There is an x: (for every y: y is A if and only if $y = x$) and (x is B).

As a little reflection shows, (1) means

(1')   There is *exactly one thing* that is A and *this thing* is B.

(1) is the proposed transcription of '*The* A is B'. 'The A' is of course the descriptive phrase. To see what is achieved, consider an example, putting 'wife of Smith' (not: '*the* wife of Smith'!) and 'blond' for '*A*' and '*B*' respectively. If Smith has (exactly) one wife, then (1) will, by virtue of the clause in the second parenthesis, be true if she is blond; false, if she isn't. If he has either no wife or more than one, (1) will be false by virtue of the clause in the first parenthesis. Thus we can, without violating the Hamlet-principle and without running into trouble if Smith happens to be a bachelor (or a polygamist) speak, as we must, about what we cannot name because it is not in front of our nose.

Some readers who understood well what has been said so far but who do not know anything else about these matters may have wondered how one could ever make good the very far-reaching syntactical claim on p. 42. Sentences of the form 'All A are B' are in English simple clauses; yet they are not in the subject-predicate form since the two letters mark the places of two predicates. The way we transcribed all- and some-statements eliminates the difficulty in this case and thus lends some credence to the general claim. E.g., 'For every x: if x is A then x is B', is compounded from the two subject-predicate schemata 'x is A' and 'x is B' by means of 'if-then' and 'all (for every x)'.

What happens if one transcribes the 'exist' in 'Peter exists'? The transcription is 'There is an x: x is Peter'. Being a proper name, 'Peter' cannot stand in the predicate place. Thus, if we insist that the 'is' signifies what it signifies when it stands between subject and predicate, the transcription is not a sentence but nonsense. The one way out is to assume that the 'is' signifies identity. But in this case the sentence becomes redundant (technically, unlike some other redundant sentences, a tautology). For all it says then is that there is something that is identical with Peter. But Peter, like everything, is identical with itself.

Notice, finally, that the 'is' in the inseparable phrase 'there is' (German: *es gibt*, French: *il y a*) is neither the 'is' of identity nor the subject-predicate 'is'. An improved language would therefore use three different signs!

DEFINITION

Children in school are asked by their teachers to describe elephants, lions, tigers, and other animals which they may or may not have seen in zoos. When a child asked to describe an elephant answers that it has horns and a mane, the teacher tells him that what he said was false. Speaking as we do, we would have to say that the child had been asked to define 'elephant'. *All definitions are analytically true.* How, then, can what the child said be false? The answer is not difficult. The child's shortcoming may be either of two kinds; probably it was a mixture of both. He may not have paid sufficiently close attention to a certain kind of objects with which he was familiar, either directly or through pictures; and he may have failed to learn what 'elephant' has been made to mean in English. He may, for instance, have described an okapi. Words mean what they are made to mean; after they have been given meanings, one can make mistakes or display linguistic ignorance by using them differently. It is to this latter error that the teacher's "false" applies. What is the lesson of this simple tale?

We learn many words directly and more or less unsystematically, either by hearing them used in certain situations to which they are appropriate or by simply "picking up" their use from others. Yet we could, in principle, learn them by being presented with their definitions. The undefined vocabulary of an improved language corresponds roughly to the class of words one could not, even in principle, learn in this manner. This, by the way, illustrates nicely how the analyst uses the phrase 'in principle'. In principle it is possible to acquire most of one's vocabulary by means of definitions, yet it is both a practical and a psychological impossibility. But this is nevertheless the principle or the logic of the situation. It is most closely approximated when scientists invent entirely new words. Chemists probably do that more often than others; and when the layman reads one of these words, say, on the label of a prescription, he knows that the sounds his lips form betoken an English word only by virtue of a rather complex set of circumstances (of which he of course need not be conscious at the moment). The situation is characteristically different when scientists choose an existing word, making it what is called a technical term by endowing it definitionally with a precise meaning. The difference is that this practice can become the source of all sorts of pseudoproblems and confusions. Take 'force'. For a long time now in mechanics it has served as an abbreviation for the product of mass and acceleration and for nothing else. This was not always so. At an early stage, in the eighteenth century, the term was still used ambiguously or alternatively for the three different things that are now called force, momentum, and kinetic energy. The Latin and the German terms for the last (*vis viva, lebendige Kraft*) are, as it were, linguistic fossils of that stage. There was even some discussion then, among very distinguished men, about which of the three was really "force." Of this presently. Let me first sum up what we have learned so far.

Technically, a definition is the addition of a new word to a language. Technically, in proposing a definition one speaks, therefore, not within but about the language whose vocabulary is being enriched. After one has agreed to add, say, 'stallion' as an abbreviation for 'male horse', one can, within the language, form the sentence 'a stallion is a male horse'. Technically, this sentence is an analytic truth. To see this, quite nontechnically, one merely has to consider that it is not a factual statement about horses; it is merely the expression within the language of an agreement about the use of a word. Thus it would be foolish indeed to look either at horses or at anything else to find out whether or not it is true. Definitions are, quite aptly, called linguistic truths. (This phrase, we remember, is also used to characterize analyticity. So it may suggest that tautologies are true "by definition." As it happens, this is one of the occasions where the formula that calls analytic truth linguistic is misleading, for it over-generalizes from the case of definitions. The truth of, say, 'it is raining or it isn't', reflect as it does the logical structure of the world (another formula!), is not just a "linguistic convention" in the sense in which all definitions are such conventions.) A definition, finally, is merely an abbreviation. In principle all definitions are therefore expendable. Practically, we shall soon see, there is another side to this particular feature of definitions. Another practical point may as well be mentioned now. It will be remembered that there is sometimes more than one way in which a class of synthetic propositions can be divided into the axioms and the theorems of a theory (p. 31). There are sometimes similar choices in the combined class of (the prospective) axioms, theorems, and definitions of a theory. Schematically speaking, if of two propositions containing a certain term one is chosen as defining the term, then the other becomes an axiom or theorem; and conversely. In some cases the situation is more complex than that. Newton's so-called laws of motion are probably the best known among the cases in which this insight is a powerful tool of analysis. But I must not tarry with this delightful case. The one thing valuable for our purposes is this. As we ordinarily speak, one can never be sure whether what someone says is, logically, a definition or a statement of fact. If we cannot ask him or if he does not appreciate our question, all we can do is watch him. If he does not look for positive evidence or, even better, if presented with what some take to be negative evidence he brushes it aside as irrelevant, then we can be rather sure that what he said was, whether he knew it or not, logically a definition. In an improved language or, within science, in an articulate theory this sort of ambiguity cannot occur. In the less well developed behavior sciences some confusions flow, or flowed until recently, from this rather shallow source. This brings us back to where we left another strain of thought.

To adopt a definition for an existing word is both to sharpen and to narrow its meaning or, sometimes, as with 'force', to add an entirely new and precise meaning to the one or several vague ones it has had before. This is particularly striking in the case of "psychological" words such as 'intelligence', 'personality', 'habit', and so on. With respect to them one also hears very frequently the complaint that when they are used only with the precise meaning given to them by definition, something is lost. To appraise this complaint or objection, consider 'force'; for there is in this respect no difference between 'force' and, say, 'intelligence'. To get at the heart of the matter, we must first introduce a distinction among concepts.

A concept is neither true nor false, only propositions are. A concept is neither valid nor invalid, only arguments are (p. 29). Yet there is a distinction of "good" and "bad" among defined descriptive concepts. To have a name for it, I shall say that a concept either is or is not *significant*. A concept is significant if and only if it occurs, together with others, in statements of lawfulness which we have reason to believe are true. It follows that some concepts are, in an inherently vague sense that cannot and need not be made precise, "more" significant than others. For instance, a concept that occurs only in one or two tentative and isolated laws is "less" significant than one that occurs in a well-established theory of considerable scope. It follows, furthermore, that what is not significant today may become so tomorrow. But I had better put some flesh on the bare bones of these statements.

Sometimes 'meaningful' is used synonymously with 'significant'. This is one of the technical meanings one may plausibly assign to 'meaning'. But then one should be aware that 'meaning' is often also used in another technical sense. In this sense, every correctly defined term, whether significant or not, is "meaningful." For a term to be correctly defined its fully expanded definition must be a grammatically correct sentence that contains except for the term itself only undefined descriptive terms. I say fully expanded because practically definitions come in chains or hierarchies. Starting from the undefined descriptive vocabulary, one first states one group of definitions, then adds the terms so defined to the basic descriptive vocabulary and uses this enlarged class in the next group of definitions, and so on. An improved language contains only terms that are either undefined or meaningful in the sense of being correctly defined. This is in fact one of its major virtues.

Assume that somebody proposes a new concept, call it the C-coefficient. A person's C-coefficient is, by definition, the number obtained by multiplying his white blood count by his weight in ounces and dividing the product by the number of hairs on his legs. Clearly, it is not difficult to ascertain a person's C-coefficient. Equally clearly, the concept is not significant. Why, one may ask, are we so certain of this? After all, there could be laws in which it occurs. In principle this is so. Yet we are very certain that there are none. To understand the reasons we have for this certainty, assume that the proponent of our new concept is a crank who expects to use it for the prediction of cancer, that is, he hopes to find a law that makes the incidence of cancer a function of his C-coefficient ('C' from 'cancer'!). Again, why do we call him a crank? The point is that we do know a good deal about cancer, and that neither the C-coefficient itself nor the law our friend expects to find "fits" with the existing laws and theories about cancer. What goes for cancer goes for the whole of biology. That is why we are so certain that the C-coefficient is not significant. There would be no point in trying to make this notion of "fitting" more precise. Once in a while, though less frequently the more we already know, the crank of today is indeed the genius of tomorrow. Be that as it may, the story illustrates the guidance we receive, negatively, from laws and theories in the elimination of concepts that are not significant. Just as important, or perhaps even more so, is the guidance laws and theory afford, positively, in the "discovery" of significant concepts. (I shall give a detailed illustration in the second chapter.) This is the practical point I mentioned before when I said that definitions are merely abbreviations and, therefore, in principle expendable. Practically, and for the same reason, namely, the way our minds are constituted, we could no more do without defined concepts than we could do without deductive inferences. Thus the following statements supplement rather than contradict each other. Logically, deductive inference yields nothing new. Practically, we could not get along without it. Logically, definitions are analytic. Practically, the "discovery" of a significant concept is often the decisive step in the discovery (without quotation marks!) of laws and the formulation of theories. The distinction involved is worth noting explicitly. The logical analysis of science is one thing; the psychology of discovery is another thing. The former is a philosophical enterprise; the latter, if we only knew more about it, would be a branch of the science of psychology. To demand that the former conform or do justice—I hardly know how to put it—to the facts of the latter is a source of confusion to both. The father of this confusion is Hegel; its American foster father is John Dewey.

What light does all this throw on our original questions about 'force' and 'intelligence'? Interestingly, the three different defined characters that are now called force, momentum, and kinetic energy respectively and that at one time competed for the appellation 'force' all proved to be highly significant. That is why each of them has a name of its own. But there are also certain relations that obtain among them, partly by definition, partly by law. As for the original undefined 'force' of ordinary speech, one could not without violence say that any of the three defined concepts is a more precise version of it. If one tried, rather pointlessly, to define it in an improved language, one would first of all have to discard its meta-phorical uses, as in 'He is a forceful person'. The residue would have to be defined in terms of certain kinaesthetic sensations. The only connection between this "force" and the three defined scientific notions is through the laws that connect the occurrence of those sensations with the forces, mo-menta, and amounts of kinetic energy applied to or by the body of their owners. This, however, we know only in retrospect. In some cases, though, we have prospectively some more or less vague hunches or insights into such connections that guide us in the definition of concepts as well as in the choice of the names we give them; and the names may in turn guide our thought. This is again a point in the psychology of discovery. To safe-guard it, one need not deny any of our analytical distinctions and clarifica-tions. In other words, the apprehension that something gets lost if one proceeds by "arbitrary" definition is without ground. This apprehension and the objections to which it gives rise have long been rampant in psy-chology. So I shall be tedious rather than too brief and say the same thing all over again in the case of 'intelligent' and its derivatives. To make it an undefined term is out of the question. It is much too "abstract" for that by any serious criterion of acquaintance. Also, its ordinary use is much too vague and, as everybody admits, ambiguous. IQ is, as things go in psy-chology, a well-defined notion, as precise as, say, our crank's C-coefficient. Again, those who gave it its name did this because they expected to dis-cover some laws connecting it with some of those kinds of behavior that determine, among several others, quite unsystematically yet quite indubit-ably, the ordinary use of 'intelligence'. In this respect there is no difference between them and our crank. The only difference is that they in fact dis-covered such laws. This shows that the formula, "intelligence is what the IQ measures," which some psychologists hurled at those who harassed them with silly objections, is less than half the truth. It is really silly itself. One could spin out the comparison with 'force'. One might imagine, for instance, that after the discovery of a few more significant concepts such as IQ one will be able to devise in terms of them further definitions each of which corresponds more or less accurately to one of the several meanings of the original 'intelligent'. I say more or less because what is inherently vague can, in an obvious sense, not be made precise. On the other hand, one could, if one only knew enough, predict accurately each occurrence of these vague uses. But I have surely said enough.

All definitions are what I just called them, *arbitrary*. The word indicates aptly the more strictly logical side of the nature of definitions. Whether or not a term we have defined is significant depends of course on the facts and not on us. But we are free to frame "arbitrarily" any definition we can think of. This freedom is the starting point of the following line of reasoning. One can "make" definitions, but one cannot, in the same sense, make things. Thus one cannot expect that every defined character word "names" something that "exists." There are two reasonable alternatives. Either only some defined terms name existents or none of them do. The first alternative is at the core of Aristotelianism. Aristotle taught that it was the main task of science to discover the correct definitions (the technical term is 'real definition') of what exists. The second alternative is one of the central ideas in the main stream of modern rationalism. For our purposes we shall not need to pay much attention to the first; whoever does not understand the second cannot make sense out of large parts of the development that will occupy us in Volume Three. The best opportunity to lay the ground for such understanding is right here. The way I put the argument—since all definitions are arbitrary, no defined term names what exists—makes it clear that the issue is once more *the existential status of abstract concepts*. (Technically, one speaks rather of ontological status, but I am avoiding the technical terms of philosophy proper. 'Rationalism' I use simply as the name for this type of argument. The name is historically justified.) Happily, we are by now able to see through this line of reasoning. It is not really an argument but merely one of those verbal tangles that can be built up by speaking "philosophically." As for 'exist', it makes no sense whatsoever to say that the referents of defined predicates do or do not "exist." Such a character either is or is not exemplified. If it is, then a certain there-is statement is true; if it is not, then the statement is false. Moreover, if one insists, rather pointlessly and confusingly, on using 'exist', then he ought to realize that what the there-is statement states the "existence" of is an instance of the character and not the character itself. As for 'naming', we disentangled it from 'existing'. Thus there is no difficulty in saying, conveniently and quite naturally, that a defined predicate that contains nonvacuously at least one that is undefined names a character. This disposes of the rationalist argument. However, it will pay off later to explore now the intellectual motive behind it.

Notice the ambiguity of the phrase I just used, the existential status of abstract concepts. Unambiguously, I should have spoken of the status of what these concepts (words) name or purport to name. Of course, I introduced the blur deliberately; for it reflects, down to the very word 'concept', the rationalist pattern. The basic idea is this. What "experience" presents to us, or what "exists" in the world outside of our minds, put it any way you want, is merely some sort of shapeless stuff, perhaps what is properly named by proper names; all "concepts," including, if one wants to be consistent, the undefined ones, that shape this stuff are contributed by the mind. Now the intellectual motive is clear. The "abstract concepts" are denied status "in the world" in order to locate them the more securely "in the mind," thus aggrandizing the latter by making its content, or at least the shape of it, independent of "experience."

There is also a version, really more consistent in some respects, according to which the abstract entities are laid up in some sort of Platonic heaven. The appeal of this view is that upon it we do not "make" the abstract things, in a foolish sense of 'making'. Its difficulty is to account for their "getting into" our minds on the proper occasions. At this point the deity was appealed to. But all this is detail that need not concern us since it does not seem to have influenced the development of psychology. Its whole atmosphere, unlike that of the main stream, was too esoteric and unscientific for that. Yet it was one of the more ingenious intellectual constructions. The name connected with it is Malebranche's. Its remote ancestor is Augustine.

British and German psychology from Locke to Wundt cannot be understood unless it is seen as a struggle against this pattern. As far as the "ideas" or "concepts" of "abstract" things are concerned, its basic idea, analytic introspection, though not always the execution of this idea, makes sense. The dialectical balance is delicate, though. How is one to find one's way around intellectually, if, rejecting the rationalist pattern, one yet cannot, as we did, in one's own way account for the abstract things themselves (not their "concepts" or "ideas")? The product of this embarrassment is an awkward position known as radical empiricism. Radical empiricists harbor a profound suspicion against "abstract" things. To them, all such things smack of rationalism and are "fictions" at best. In the philosophy of science the suspicion becomes a bias against all highly defined concepts. Nor does it stop there. Typically, the basic terms of a theory are, as we saw (p. 33), highly defined. Thus theory itself becomes suspect. The most influential representative of this tendency was, perhaps, Ernst Mach. Its most vigorous advocate among contemporary psychologists is Skinner. He thinks that the "abstract" concepts of behavior theory, no matter how "objectively" and "operationally" defined they may be (I am again merely parading these two words), portend a covert revival of "mentalism" or "antibehaviorism." I know of only one way to explain so strange an aberration. Skinner's is the radical empiricist's suspicion of "abstract" terms. They are the stalking horses of rationalism, and rationalism is the champion of "mind." Hence, psychological "theory" is inherently "mentalistic" and, therefore, not good "behaviorism." Queer. Yet it is also delightful to discover all these subterranean connections, to formulate, if I may so put it, the unconscious grammar of the unanalyzed metaphysics which so many philosophically inclined scientists carry around with them without knowing it. *Plus ça change, plus c'est la même chose.*

All defined terms are *eliminable;* that is, for every sentence containing a defined term there is another, analytically equivalent to it (i.e., meaning the same thing) that does not contain the term. Syntactically this is the essence of definitions. Some clarifications, though, depend on a closer examination of their syntactical form. So I turn now to such an examination.

The basic idea is that of a weighing balance in equilibrium. In one pan, conventionally the left, is the new term, called *definiendum* ('. . . . .'); in the other pan, the defining term or phrase, called the *definiens* ('oooooo'). If we write schematically

'. . . . .' for 'oooooo',

the 'for' will indicate the agreed upon sameness of meaning as well as remind us that defined terms are eliminable abbreviations. This basic idea is of course sound. However, most definitions are not that simple. Ordinarily, the left side is not the definiendum in isolation but an entire sentence, namely, the (schema of the) simplest sentence in which the new term occurs as a predicate. The right side, too, is a sentence, usually a compound sentence. An illustration will help. Take 'alive', as applied to a wire in which an electric current flows. The left side reads 'x is alive'. One possible definiens is 'If a magnetic needle is brought close to x, then it will show a deviation'. This is of course a very crude, merely qualitative, and in one respect (how close is close?) rather vague definition. This is beside the point. Illustrations ought above all to be simple. Also, many definitions in the behavior sciences are as yet just as crude. But one may wonder why I chose an illustration that seems so awkward, since instead of 'x is alive' one would much rather say 'There is an electric current in x', thus "defining" the familiar and impressively abstract 'electric current' instead of the idiomatic and slightly quaint 'alive'. I created this awkwardness deliberately in order to bring out some points. In an improved language, what one defines is always a predicate ('P', 'R'); the left side is always the schema of the sentence stating that something has the character in question ('x is P', 'x is in relation R to y'); it is never a there-is statement like 'There is an electric current in x'. 'Electric current', finally, is a much more complex notion that cannot be defined so simply. It depends on a model, originally a "hypothetical" fluid.

Since the definiens is a schema in which the new term occurs as a predicate, one may wonder how to eliminate it from sentences in which it occurs as a subject. In languages with a certain syntactical property known as extensionality this can be done. There is reason to believe that the ideal language and all improved languages required for more limited purposes are extensional. This does not hold for their "linguistic part," though (p. 22). This part must and can be dealt with separately. Besides, it certainly plays no role in the analysis of scientific statements, including those of the behavior sciences. The behavior scientist speaks among other things about language, namely the linguistic behavior of his subjects. But a little reflection shows that such statements are not "linguistic" in our sense.

The definiens of our illustration is an if-then compound. This is typical. Most worthwhile definitions are of this form. Such definitions are called *operational;* the concepts they define, *dispositional.* Each of these terms, as it became fashionable, was the vehicle of some clarifications and of some confusions. "Operationism" in the last generation swept psychology and is rather influential in the other behavior sciences. The notion of dispositional concepts and properties is by now, alas, mainly a source of confusions. So I shall start with the former.

Take a wire, call it '*a*', put '*a*' for '*x*' in our definition, call the left side of what you obtain *L,* the right side *R. L* reads 'a is alive'. *R* is an if-then statement. To know whether *L* is true one must know whether *R* is. Since 'alive' is a "new" word, there is indeed no other way of finding out. Again, if one knows nothing else, there is only one way of ascertaining the truth of so simple an if-then statement as *R.* One must look and see whether the antecedent (i.e., the sentence between 'if' and 'then') is true. If the antecedent is true, then the compound statement *R* is true if and only if the consequent (i.e., the sentence following 'then') is true. If the antecedent is false, one cannot tell. If there is no magnetic needle close to *a* (and if we know nothing else), we can therefore not tell whether '*a* is alive' is true. But we can find out by performing certain operations, that is, manipulations, namely, by bringing a magnetic needle close to *a.* Then we can tell. If the needle shows a deviation, 'a is alive' is true; if it does not, the sentence is false. This is the whole of "operationism." To ascertain the truth or falsehood of a statement in which a defined term of this kind occurs—and, I repeat, most worthwhile definitions are of this kind—one must perform certain manipulations and observe what happens. Strictly, I have shown this only for the simplest sentence in which the defined term occurs; but the generalization is both plausible and not difficult; so I shall say no more about it. In the case of a quantified concept, the antecedent of *R* describes the measuring procedure; the consequent describes its result, e.g., the coincidence of a pointer with a certain mark on a scale. As far as it goes, the point is well taken. It is worth noticing that the very definition of a scientific term states what one must do and what, having done it, one must see in order to assert the truth of the simplest statement in which the term occurs. But one may well wonder how this footnote to the analysis of definitions could ever have aroused such enthusiasm that it was mistaken for the whole of the philosophy of science.

The fashion had its origin in physics. If one wanted to, one could describe one of Einstein's achievements, the one that led to the theory of relativity, in two sentences as follows. First, he recognized that 'nonlocally simultaneous' cannot plausibly be included among the undefined relation terms of a "realistic" language. Second, he proposed an "operational" definition for this term that proved spectacularly significant. Inspired by his success, some philosophically minded physicists convinced themselves and their readers that all concepts of physics, however "abstract" they may be, can be so defined.

This is not literally true, though, for those concepts that are introduced not by definition but by the interpretation of axiomatic calculi (p. 37). The concepts of quantum mechanics must be so introduced (p. 124). Of such concepts the operational enthusiasts made indeed a pretty mess. Some of them were also guilty of some of the confusions which I shall presently attribute to some psychologists.

Among their most avid readers were the psychologists, among them especially the "behaviorists." * As I hinted before and as we shall see in great detail in Volume Two, the main tenet of the latter is the adequacy for psychology of a "realistic" language (criterion (1″), p. 40). This is why psychologists sometimes don't even bother to distinguish between "behaviorism" and "operationism." What attracted them above all in the latter was, therefore, the emphasis on the adequacy of the undefined vocabulary of a "realistic" language for all purposes of physics, including theoretical physics. Thus one might expect operationism to have stimulated the growth of theory in psychology. For, if physics was able to erect the imposing structure of its abstract concepts and sweeping theories on that firm and narrow basis, why couldn't the same be done in psychology? Yet this is not what happened, at least not in the beginning, during the thirties. Quite to the contrary, the operationist formulae, half understood, were for a while used as a stick to beat all theory. The causes of this *contretemps* are not hard to find. There is, first, the fact that the concepts of what then still passed for psychological theory were ill defined by any standard. Secondly, most of these so-called theories were closely identified with the "antibehaviorist" claims concerning the inadequacy, for psychological purposes, of a "realistic" language. Thirdly, some of the protagonists of the day were tainted with "radical empiricism." There are in any field and at any time people who dislike abstract concepts and theory, some of them meticulous experimenters and ingenious gadgeteers, some just unimagina-

---

* Perhaps this is as good a place as any to smooth whatever feathers I have ruffled by the lavish use of double quotes. Semantical or single quotes, the intelligent reader realizes, are indispensable in this sort of discussion. But why all those double quotes? Behaviorism, for instance, is a respectable word and the author himself, or so it would seem, is some sort of behaviorist. The point is that for the most part these words are used ambiguously, vaguely, and even misleadingly, as verbal bridges, as I like to call them, to cover the absence of real argument. In a sense, and I put it strongly for the sake of making a point, the whole philosophy of science is nothing but the meticulous explication of a score or so of these words. Also, one could do quite well without virtually any of them. If I use them at all, it is partly for the sake of brevity, and in this case I define them first; partly because I wish to indicate which positions I am analyzing.

tive. When psychology was hit by the operationist fad, it was absorbing quite an influx of such people. The causes of this influx must be sought in the social climate of American psychology with its heavy emphasis on social engineering. A "radical empiricist" or an "operationist" is of course himself a thinker. But one can easily understand why their thought was welcomed as an ideological defense by the doers. The attendant misunderstandings have by now happily disappeared; at least they have been pointed out. But it may still be worth while to review them briefly.

While operations in the relevant sense are manipulations and nothing else, the "operationists" saw operations everywhere. At the one extreme, the scientist's observations were decked out to be a species of operations; at the other, his verbal and computational activities were, as so-called symbolic operations, herded into the same corral. Such completely non-specific use of 'operation' (or of any word) is not only useless; it is also confusing. And there was still another confusion. To give an extreme illustration, some refused, presumably on operationist principles, to "generalize" from one instance of an experiment to the next if the apparatus had in the meantime been moved to another corner of the room or if the experimenter had, in the one case but not in the other, blown his nose. To see through this error one must grasp two important ideas. For one thing, there is no such thing as an exhaustive description. For another, there are no rules that lead automatically to the discovery of relevant variables. (I shall have to say a good deal about the notion of a relevant variable in the next chapter. But what must be said now needs, I trust, no preparation.) Neither "operationism" nor, for that matter, the philosophy of science furnishes any rules for discovery either of significant definitions or of laws. Take a primitive notion of length, defined in terms of the layings-off of a yardstick. As it happens, the rule specifies that the yardstick should not be made of soft rubber. As it also happens, it does not, because it need not, specify that the yardstick must not be twirled around between successive layings-off. It need not, because a definition of length that omits this prohibition from among its clauses proves nonetheless to be significant. But, again, "operationism" has nothing to say about that. To repeat, there is no canon which, if followed, leads automatically to the discovery of significant concepts. A concept "operationally defined" may yet be utterly devoid of significance. The atmosphere of these comments is, I think, quite unmistakable. Some of the early "operationist" emphasis was not only mistaken but also rather petty. It is only fair to point out, though, that all this concrete-mindedness was at least in part an understandable reaction to the fuzzy-mindedness in other psychological quarters. So it was probably wholesome that psychology went through this phase.

If one wants to know how high a mountain is and if one knows nothing from which its height could be inferred, then one must measure it. To measure it, one must perform certain operations. But both the mountain and its height are there ("exist"), whether or not we measure the latter. Thus we shall not be tempted to say that we "made" either of them, in some foolish sense of 'making'. In the case of the edge of a table, which we may have made, there are two different operations, that of making the table and that of measuring its edge. Involved here is, once more, the "existence" of abstract objects. Wise as we are to the pitfalls of 'exist', we avoid all such wrangles. Yet it is curious to note that "operationism" has been misused to support a modern version of the rationalist doctrine about abstract objects. Naturally, the matter has not been put quite as simply and as bluntly as I just did, in terms of mountains and tables. Generally, if certain things had been said the way the analyst says them afterwards, they probably wouldn't have been said at all. In the case at hand, the basic idea of the spurious doctrine is that we introduce into what is in itself an "indeterminate situation" our concepts or operations—the distinction between the two is deliberately and artfully blurred—as "instruments" with which to "determine" it according to our purposes. Both the words and the doctrine are those of Deweyan "instrumentalism." Dewey himself is a direct intellectual descendant of the archrationalist Hegel. Like all rationalist doctrines, instrumentalism exaggerates the role of man in the universe. In this respect there is no difference. The difference is that while classical rationalism aggrandizes man the thinker, instrumentalism exalts man the doer. Accordingly, while in classical rationalism the ambiguous 'concept' blurs into 'idea', in instrumentalism it blurs into 'operation'. To see how futile it is to introduce "operationism" into this context, one merely has to consider that it does not make the slightest difference whether what the antecedent of a definition in the if-then form states is being brought about deliberately by us or, as one says, by chance. Practically, if we want to know whether certain statements are true, we must perform certain manipulations, just as we must act if we want to survive. In principle and if we had only time enough, we could wait until certain things occur. For what matters logically is only that they occur, not that we cause them to occur.

I undertook to explicate 'operational' and 'dispositional'. I have done with the first. So I turn to the second.

When we say that a man is angry, we may mean that he is in a state of anger, that is, that he either has certain feelings or both has them and expresses them by certain kinds of overt behavior. But we also sometimes call a person angry when he is not at the time in a state of anger. In this case we mean that he would, upon slighter provocation than most other people, either have those feelings or both have them and overtly express them. If one wanted to speak more accurately, avoiding the rather harmless ambiguity which 'angry' has in this respect, one would say in the second case that the person is irascible or that he is of an angry *disposition*. What one thus calls a disposition is always a complex and implicitly relational character whose definiens is of the if-then form. This is also the sense in which 'disposition' and 'dispositional' have been used in recent philosophical discussions. Most, if not all, personality traits are dispositional characters. So is habit, if it is defined in a certain way. (By this qualification, if it is defined in a certain way, hangs quite a tale. But of this presently; the tale does not belong to the story about dispositions.) The property of being soluble (in water) is an example from another area. Salt, for instance, though it is soluble, is not always dissolving. By calling it soluble we mean that *if* it is put into water, it dissolves. As I have pointed out more than once, virtually all scientific concepts are dispositional in this sense, which is the only clear sense of the term. Consider length. For a rod to be of length three means, by definition, that *if* the unit yardstick is laid off against it in the familiar fashion starting from one of its ends, its other end will at the third laying-off coincide with the end of the unit stick. Yet we do not ordinarily speak or think of a rod's length as one of its "dispositions." Now there is nothing wrong with using a term technically in a broader sense than when we use it nontechnically. In this case, though, it is of some interest to inquire what additional features must be present for a dispositional property to be called a "disposition" when we speak as the tongue runs. The subtleties of usage are so elusive and, for the most part, so irrelevant to philosophical issues, that there is no point in trying to compile a complete list of these features. Two kinds of situations stand out, however. We speak, I think, of a disposition if, when the condition stated in the antecedent of the definition is realized, a change occurs in the object that exemplifies the defined character. Salt, when put into water, dissolves. A brittle object—brittleness is, rather obviously, a dispositional character—shatters when hit or knocked. Nothing so drastic happens to the rod that is being measured. In the other kind of situation one is, I think, guided by the idea of the object in question possessing another more or less permanent and less patently dispositional property which, if the condition stated in the antecedent is realized, interacts with it to bring about what is stated in the consequent. In the case of personality traits, for instance, one may think of or imagine some such property of a person's "mind" or, for that matter, of his body. Again, we neither know nor imagine any such property connected with length. This is all there is to the notion of a disposition—except for a confusion that stems from failure to understand certain issues belonging to philosophy proper and that belongs therefore, in this book, in small print.

There is no argument in philosophy proper about the adequacy of the definitions of dispositions by if-then statements. Whatever argument there is, and there has been a good deal of it lately, is about whether a certain formalization of these definitions is adequate. If we do not construct our improved language syntactically, which we saw the philosopher of science need not do, there is therefore no argument whatsoever.

Assume that the antecedent of such a definition has not been realized; for instance, that a certain powder was burned before it had ever been put into water. As long as we speak ordinarily we would say, as I did a while ago, that in this case and if we know nothing else about the powder, we could not tell whether or not it was soluble. If the language is formalized in the manner in which it must be formalized if certain philosophical problems are to become explicable by means of it, then the 'if-then' in our definitions becomes a logical word (connective) and the statement that the powder was soluble would be counted as true. This awkwardness invites further analysis. Some analysts believe that such analysis reveals it to be rather harmless and that a schema which does not avoid it is therefore adequate. Others disagree. This and only this is the issue. But there is again no disagreement on another point, namely, that the only way to avoid the awkwardness in the improved schema is to represent the 'if-then' of our definitions by a nonlogical word. Quite nontechnically speaking, such a nonlogical 'if-then' could be used to state in the improved schema not only 'If the powder is put into water it dissolves' but also 'If the powder *were* put into water, it *would* dissolve'. Obviously, this would eliminate the awkwardness (though not increase our knowledge about the powder in the situation I assumed). The logical 'if-then', on the other hand, that is, the 'if-then' of the desired formalization, cannot be made to express the subjunctive. At this point the issue is connected with another, in which a certain philosophical use of 'disposition' plays a key role.

In the formalizations which so many philosophical problems require for their solution, laws are, as we saw (p. 47), generalized if-then statements of which the simplest paradigm is 'For every x: If x is A then x is B', where the 'if-then' is again the logical or connective 'if-then'. Consequently there is, as I shall not show in detail, no way of distinguishing, *by simply looking at the statement itself*, between a so-called accidental generality and a "genuine" law of nature. For an amusing example of an accidental generality that has been used in these discussions consider the case of a bench in a certain park in Boston on which during all its lifetime only Irishmen sat. 'For every x: if x sits on this bench then x is Irish' would be a generality and true. Yet one would call it an accidental generality rather than a law of nature. Those who defend the adequacy of the Russellian formalism insist that there is a way of making this distinction by means of it, though one can't tell the difference by just looking at the generality (in the improved language) itself. Others disagree. But again, there is no disagreement that the difference could be marked in the generality itself if the 'if-then' that occurs in it could, in the case of a "genuine" law, be replaced by a nonlogical word, namely, the same nonlogical or subjunctive 'if-then' which also eliminates the awkwardness of nonsubjunctive operational definition in such cases as that of the powder. But all this is merely preparatory to a point I wish to make about "dispositions."

To know laws is virtually the same thing as to know causes. If the statement of the generality includes that of a certain temporal structure, then we say that any instance of its antecedent is the cause of the corresponding instance of its consequent. According to one view of causation, made famous by David Hume, this is, details apart, all there is to the analysis of 'cause'. Upon another view, there is something specific, a power or a *disposition,* in the object or circumstance which we call cause, and it is this something which "brings about" the effect. This disposition, being a something, would in an improved language be named by a nonlogical or descriptive word. Roughly speaking, the nonlogical 'if-then' which we encountered twice already could represent this peculiar character in the ideal language. This is of course an eminently philosophical use of 'disposition'. Negatively stated, the essence of Hume's analysis of cause is that there is no such character or characters.

I find it hard to believe that many of those who now drag fragments of these philosophical arguments into the discussion of psychological concepts really know what these arguments are about. Some rejoice, for instance, that "operationism" (or "behaviorism"?) has presumably been shown to be inadequate because of the alleged inadequacy of if-then definitions (not of a certain way to formalize them, which is quite a different matter). Do they realize that all they do in taking this position is to embrace a non-Humean position on causation? And is not, logically, either view on causation compatible with either view on "operationism" and "behaviorism"?

Earlier in this discussion of definition we examined the following argument. To insist that all terms except those of a rather narrow basic vocabulary be introduced by definition and that they be, in science, used only as defined is to incur a loss of "meaning," to deprive one's self of the guidance provided by a freer usage. The argument drew and perhaps still draws most of its devotees from the students of behavior; quite understandably, since the terms we use when we speak nonscientifically about people have acquired a rich halo, from personal experience as well as from the wisdom of the ages, that is, from the characterological and sociological insights enshrined in the humanistic tradition. Yet the argument rests, as we saw, on a simple confusion, the failure to distinguish—as it has been put, very felicitously, I think—between the context of discovery and the context of justification. More often than not it is a rather transparent rationalization of the old prejudice against any science of behavior. Yet there are, within science and its philosophy, certain questions in this general area that require answers. Let me begin with an example.

I just defined 'being alive' by the deviation of a magnetic needle; or, as I shall now say, speaking as one usually does, I defined 'electric current' in terms of a current's magnetic effects. Call the right side of this definition R_1. Nothing is easier than to think of alternative definitions of 'current', say, in terms of a current's thermic (heating of certain kinds of wire) or chemical effects (precipitation out of certain kinds of solution). Call these alternative definientia R_2 and R_3; the three definitions, D_1, D_2, D_3 respectively. Which of the three is the "correct" one? Or are all three "correct"? These are the first questions we must answer. The answers are obvious.

A definition is an agreed upon abbreviation. So there can be only one definition of a term. One makes his choice; having made it, he is committed. On the other hand, one could, if one wanted to, define three different terms, 'current$_1$' with definiens R_1, 'current$_2$' with definiens R_2, 'current$_3$' with definiens R_3. The point is that, although they name three different notions, it makes no difference which of the three we adopt as the definition of 'current'. The controlling fact is the following tripartite law L: (1) Every current$_1$ is also a current$_2$, and conversely; (2) Every current$_2$ is also a current$_3$, and conversely; (3) Every current$_3$ is also a current$_1$, and conversely. We notice in passing that any one of these three clauses, say, (1), is a deductive consequence of the other two, say, (2) and (3). But then, the statement of these two is one of fact (synthetic); and one can never hope to replace a synthetic statement by a definition, which is analytic. Thus, whichever of the three "indexed" notions one chooses as one's notion of a "nonindexed" current, one still has to state L separately. A little reflection shows that this is also the answer to a third question one might naturally ask, namely: After L has been discovered, is it not proper or, at least, expedient to choose neither R_1 nor R_2 nor R_3 as the definiens for 'current' but instead either 'R_1 or R_2 or R_3' (D_4) or, perhaps, 'R_1 and R_2 and R_3' (D_5)? In other words, does one not, or should one not, bring one's definitions up to the level of one's knowledge, namely, the just discovered L, saying that a current flows in a wire if and only if it produces either at least one of the three effects (D_4) or, perhaps, all three (D_5)? The answer is No. One may of course do so if one wishes, but nothing would be gained. L still has to be stated separately.

The preceding paragraph contains the explication of what follows. As a science progresses, its concepts become, as one says, richer in "meaning." But this does not mean that they require redefinition. Meaning, in this particular sense of the glittering word, is what we called significance. Such "meaning" of a term is not carried by its definition, but by the laws in which it occurs. This is not to say that redefinition, that is, literally, the abandonment of one concept and the introduction of another (perhaps without changing the word), is not sometimes advantageous. For instance, after one has discovered the law of thermic expansion or, in other words, the dependence of yardstick length on temperature, one will with advantage include a clause specifying a standard temperature in the definition of length and thus, in principle, replace one concept by another. But again, one must not overestimate the difference. Whether or not this is done, one must, when he makes a careful length measurement, also measure temperature. The most one can gain by redefinition is an increase in what the mathematicians call elegance. In psychology these points have recently been obscured by those who speak of the "conceptual properties" of terms (concepts); the implication being that if a scientist wants to make progress he must take care to select concepts with the "right" conceptual properties. The idea of a "conceptual property" is inherently confused. If it means anything at all, then the "conceptual properties" of a term are what is expressed by the laws in which it occurs; e.g., it is a "conceptual property" of (Newtonian) mass that it is indestructible, just as it is presumably a "conceptual property" of frustration to produce aggression (p. 36). This reduces the injunction that a scientist must choose terms with the right "conceptual properties" to the tautology that a term, to be significant, must be significant. To show the confusion it nevertheless engenders, let me once again resort to syntax. Syntactically, a property is a predicate, a law is a statement. To speak, as some do, of the "conceptual properties" of concepts is, therefore, to confuse predicates with propositions. Syntactical confusions of this kind go rather deep, so deep that some of them are at the root of whole "philosophies." The philosophy here involved is the idealistic (Hegelian and, more recently, Deweyan) version of rationalism. The basic idea is that one can, by the appropriate selection of "conceptual properties" or "meanings," that is, of definitions which are analytic, somehow catch or express what must be stated as law, that is, in propositions which are synthetic. Upon this conception of science it consists, in the ideal limit, of a class of propositions that are all analytic (definitions). This is absurd. Since an overestimation of the mind's contribution or power is the hallmark of rationalism, it is also clearly rationalistic.

Laws are sometimes spoken of as stating "relations." This usage produces a similar haze around 'relation'. The paradigm of a law, 'For every x: if $A(x)$ then $B(x)$', contains in addition to the characters marked by 'A' and 'B' only the *logical* words 'if-then' and 'all'. A relation between characters, in one important meaning of the term, is a *descriptive* character (of characters, see p. 43) which they exemplify; its paradigm is '$R(A, B)$'. Unlike the confusion between properties and propositions, this one has probably not been the seed from which a philosophical system has grown. Yet it interferes with a firm grasp of the nature of relations.

Two psychological illustrations will be useful. Consider 'hunger' and 'habit'; more precisely, 'food hunger' and 'habit strength' as used in behavior theory with reference to laboratory animals. There are at least three obvious ways to define 'hunger', namely, (1) by the time interval during which the animal has been denied access to food; (2) by certain physiological characteristics, say, stomach contractions; (3) dispositionally: *if* the animal is presented with food, it approaches and consumes it. Each alternative offers possibilities of quantification; in (1), rather obviously, through the length of the time interval; in (2) through either the frequency or the amplitude of the contractions or through some index compounded of these two; in (3) either through the latency of the response or through the amount of (a standard) food consumed or, again, through some compound index. We need not go into detail. As in the case of 'current', a purely qualitative notion will do for our present purposes. The logic of the situation is the same as before. We have here three different notions, call them 'hunger$_1$', 'hunger$_2$', 'hunger$_3$'. The third is of the kind one would also nontechnically call a disposition, probably guided by the idea of hunger$_2$ as the less patently dispositional property of the animal that interacts with the presentation of food to produce the approaching and consumatory behavior. Technically, (2) is, like all notions involving measurement, also dispositional. The distinguishing feature of (1) I shall discuss later. The controlling law is much more complex than in the case of currents. Nor do we really know it at the moment, though there is a vast amount of information in this area or, if I may so express myself, knowledge "toward it." We know for instance that an animal that is both hungry$_1$ and hungry$_2$ will under certain conditions neither approach nor consume food presented to it. Thus it is not hungry$_3$. (For a comparable situation in the case of the currents, imagine that what is a current$_1$ and a current$_2$ is also a current$_3$ if and only if the wire is of copper and above a certain temperature.) To specify these conditions is the business of the scientist. Our business is merely to point out that such facts do not prove either of the three alternatives to be unsuitable candidates for the definiens of a (nonindexed) 'hunger'. All they prove is that we are mistaken when we speak of "hunger" as one thing, alternatively "measured" in one of the three ways corresponding to the definitions of the three indexed notions. In the case of 'current' this way of speaking and thinking does no harm; quite to the contrary, it reflects economically the controlling laws. In the case of 'hunger' it is misleading because it "reflects" what is not there. Finally, to hark back to the IQ example, one may imagine that the three indexed hungers are like three different "IQ's" each naming one of three characters whose presence, absence, and degree jointly determine which people we call "intelligent" when we speak as we ordinarily do. So much for 'hunger'. 'Habit strength' may be defined in either of two ways. (1) The present habit strength of a bit of behavior in an animal may be defined as the number of times or as a specified function of the number of times the animal has, under certain conditions and with certain consequences, displayed bits of behavior of this kind in the past. The details we can again leave to the scientists. We merely notice that this is not, as we ordinarily speak, a dispositional character. (2) The habit strength of a bit of behavior in an animal may be defined in terms of the frequency (or the latency, or the amplitude) with which behavior of this kind occurs *if* the animal is, under certain conditions, put into certain situations. This is, patently, a dispositional notion. Again, the scientist must specify the con-

ditions and situations I merely mentioned. But what really interests him
are the laws that connect habit$_2$ so specified with habit$_1$ as well as with
other characters such as the various hungers. On the other hand, it clearly
makes no sense to argue whether or not 'habit' is (ought to be defined as?)
a dispositional character. If definition (2) is chosen, then it is (patently)
dispositional; if definition (1) is chosen, then it isn't. Yet questions of this
sort are still sometimes discussed, either overtly or covertly. That is why
I devoted so much time to the analysis of definition or, as one also says,
of concept formation. I shall now conclude with some comments on the
alternatives (1) in the examples of 'hunger' and 'habit'.

Is it a "property" of the shirt I wear that it was bought at a certain store
or that it was laundered yesterday? As we ordinarily speak, we wouldn't
say so. Yet 'having been bought in the men's shop on Main Street' and
'having been laundered on September 22, 1954' are, syntactically, defined
predicates; and syntax, we have learned, is an indispensable guide to the
clarification of such fundamental notions as that of "property." A property
is, indeed, what is named by a predicate; and there is clearly no difference,
as far as the defined predicates themselves are concerned, between those
that name what we ordinarily speak and think of as a "property" and those
that don't. What makes the difference is, again, significance. Consider, for
instance, 'having been laundered' and 'having been dipped into cold water
while hot'. The latter is significant. So we think of it as a property and
even have a name for it, namely, 'tempered'. The law that makes it significant is, of course, 'Steel, if tempered, becomes (more) flexible'.

The characters I just mentioned and those mentioned in the two alternatives (1) above all share one feature. In each case a thing is said to have
a character *now* if and only if it has had certain properties or been in
certain relations in the *past*. Such characters I call *historical*. They are, as
we shall see, very important in psychology. Of this later; at the moment
I want to take another look at one of the examples. If steel has been
tempered (1a), it is (more) flexible (3a); it also is, as physicists know,
of a certain molecular structure (2a). In fact, they think of (2a) as a
"state," "caused" by (1a) and "causing" (3a). 'State' is merely another
name for a property or a set of properties, including relational ones, of a
thing or a set of things, which they have at a certain time and which do
(or do not) change in time according to laws which we either know or
expect to discover. The use of 'cause', (2a) being caused by (1a) and in
turn causing (3a), merely reflects the relative positions of certain laws in
the very well developed theory of solids. Aside from the absence of such
theory, there is no difference between (1a), (2a), (3a) and the three alternative definitions (1), (2), (3) of 'hunger'. (With respect to 'current',
the difference is that the three alternative definitions we considered are
all (patently) dispositional.) The characters mentioned in (1) and (1a)

are historical; those mentioned in (2) and (2a) are not (patently) dispositional; those mentioned in (3) and (3a) are. In each triple the characters are closely connected by laws. Yet physicists are not tempted to say that 'flexible', 'tempered' and 'being of such and such molecular structure' are different names of the same character. Nor do they argue which of the three, properly expanded, is the right definition of this imaginary character. In physics we just know too much (physics, not philosophy!) to say such foolish things or to argue such senseless questions. In the behavior sciences we must still be on our guard lest we do just that.

NUMBERS

Quantification is the introduction of numbers into the definition of concepts and the formulation of laws. Physics is the most thoroughly quantified of all sciences. The last to oppose it there on philosophical grounds were the Aristotelians of the school of Padua, contemporaries of Galileo. In psychology and the other behavior sciences, where quantification has been on the rise for some time, it is still the object of overenthusiastic advocacy as well as (outside of economics) sullen resistance. As in some other respects, the biological sciences occupy an intermediate position. In physics, quantification coincided with its spectacular progress; hence the proclivity to take for granted that in all areas the former alone is a necessary as well as a sufficient condition of the latter. It would seem that this is one of the causes of that strained enthusiasm. In itself quantification is of course no more a magic key or cure-all than is axiomatization. If the material available warrants it, then its advantages are indeed incomparable. To bring out clearly why this is so is the task of the philosophical analyst. But how much of it the material warrants is a question not of principle but of strategy, on which the philosophical analyst of science cannot advise its practitioners. The matter is one of tact and of judgment, the sort of thing which one must have at his finger tips. Another cause of all the stridency in favor of quantification lies, I think, in the social climate. Of late the behavior sciences have become the basis, or the alleged basis, of professions whose numerous members are rapidly acquiring managerial power and who, for better or for worse, aspire to even more. Such aspiring groups are in need of prestige symbols. The white coat of the medical man is one; the mathematical formula is another. The resistance to quantification, on the other hand, is essentially a rationalization of the old bias against a science of man. Its arguments, such as they are, repeat the patterns of some earlier philosophies, which are in part built around a spurious dichotomy, quality versus quantity, of which I shall at the end dispose in passing. The advocates of quantification are annoyed. Understandable as it is, the annoyance does not always make their arguments more judicious and temperate.

Quantification is, clearly, a proper subject for the philosophy of science in general. In this section I shall discuss it only to that extent, leaving until later two topics of special interest to psychology. One of these is statistics. The analysis of the logic of probability, on which all statistics rests, is itself a major enterprise that requires a treatise of its own. Statistics is merely a mathematical technique; the logic of probability belongs to philosophy proper and to the philosophy of physics. The little that must nevertheless be said about statistics in this book will find its natural context in the next chapter. The other topic I postpone is so-called psychophysical measurement. It fits best with the discussion of Fechner in Volume Three.

In a sense this whole chapter is merely a (very nontechnical and very partial) exploration of the distinction between the analytic and the synthetic. A brief discussion of quantification, that is, of numbers, is therefore its natural conclusion. Consider '2 + 2 = 4'. The four signs that occur in it, '2', '+', '=', '4', are logical; the proposition itself, like every proposition in which only logical signs occur, is analytic. What holds in this case holds generally. Every arithmetical sign is logical; every arithmetical proposition is analytic, either analytically true or analytically false; '2 + 3 = 4', for instance, is analytically false or contradictory, as is 'it is raining and it isn't'. This is the fundamental insight. It will always be connected with the names of Russell and Frege who at the turn of the century established it for the first time on firm ground. Into the technicalities of their contribution I can of course not enter. Yet I shall try to say a few words about it.

It may have been noticed that I spoke of arithmetical rather than of mathematical concepts and propositions. What is ordinarily called mathematics comprehends the study of arithmetic, in the broader sense of the term which I am about to explain, as well as the investigation of the deductive connections in many axiomatic systems, such as Euclidean geometry and group theory, whose study is greatly facilitated by finding arithmetical interpretations for them, in the sense in which so-called analytical geometry is an interpretation of geometry. The point of the distinction is that while both the axioms and theorems of an axiomatic system are synthetic, arithmetical propositions are analytic. Arithmetic so understood comprehends not only the elementary propositions we learn as children but the whole of so-called higher mathematics. By the end of the nineteenth century it had been established, though, that all arithmetical propositions follow deductively from some very simple ones about integers, as simple in fact as our illustration, '2 + 2 = 4'. To demonstrate the analyticity of the whole of arithmetic it therefore suffices to establish that these simple propositions themselves are analytic. For what follows deductively from analytic premisses is itself analytic. (A statement of fact cannot be deduced from one that says nothing!) Strictly speaking, this must be done in an improved language. Even there it can only be done if arithmetical ideas which are intuitively quite simple such as, for instance, the integers themselves, 1, 2, 3, and so on, are construed as defined notions, that is, if the numerals, '1', '2', '3', and so on, are introduced as defined signs. This is indeed the basic idea. To grasp it, consider the following long statement: 'Tom is a person and Dick is a person and Harry is a person and Tom is in this room and Dick is in this room and Harry is in this room and no other person is in this room'. 'Three' is so defined that the short statement 'Three persons are in this room' follows deductively from the first. Aside from the individuality of the three, their being Tom, Dick, and Harry rather than Mary, Margaret, and Martha, it is indeed equivalent to the first. As for 'three' being logical and not descriptive, consider that the first, long statement contains in addition to the three proper names only three descriptive expressions, 'person', 'this room', and 'in'. (The second is a rudimentary descriptive phrase; the third names a spatial relation.) These three occur also in the second, short statement. What additional nonlogical idea could then be hidden behind 'three'? This of course does not "prove" that 'three' is logical; the proof is much more elaborate; but it makes it plausible, I think.

Let me once again be obvious rather than obscure. Arithmetical propositions are analytic; but numbers, which are just a species of logical words, can occur in synthetic statements. 'Three persons are in this room', which contains the logical 'three', is a synthetic statement, just as is 'Peter is a lawyer or a physician', which contains the logical 'or'. To show the role arithmetical propositions play in relation to synthetic ones (and, therefore, in science) one must first elaborate the illustration. Assume we learn that four people have entered the room in which we know there were three. From the two propositions stating these two facts we can deduce 'Seven people are in this room'. To make the deduction, one adds to the two synthetic statements as an additional "premiss" the arithmetical proposition '$3 + 4 = 7$'. The latter, being analytic, is not materially a premiss; like any other tautology, it can be "added" to the premises of any argument. Naturally, the important uses of arithmetic are a bit more complicated, just as important arguments are a bit more complicated, than the examples I used a while ago. But that does not in the least affect the principle of the thing. We have come upon one of the main reasons why quantification can be of tremendous advantage. Arithmetic is a vast treasure house of additional premises, or, what amounts to the same thing, of patterns of deductive inference. Quantification is the key to the treasure. To see this clearly in another example, consider Galileo's laws of freely falling bodies. With feet (s) and seconds (t) as units and $g = 32$, they read

(1) $s = 16t^2$,   (2) $v = 32t$,   (3) $a = 32$.

Velocity (v) and acceleration (a) are defined in terms of t and s. Call these two definitions D_1 and D_2. (2) and (3) follow deductively from (1) in conjunction with D_1 and D_2. The latter two, being analytic, are as we saw legitimate additional premisses. (1) and (3) follow similarly from (2); (1) and (2) from (3). The additional premisses needed for these deductions are some of the tautologies of the differential calculus. This is the point. (Experts will recognize that I neglected the constants of integration. This is an irrelevant technicality.)

There is still another lesson to be learned from Tom, Dick, and Harry. When we passed from the long to the short statement we counted them. *Counting* is one of the two ways in which numbers enter into synthetic statements. Aside from straight counting, this way consists in the introduction of numbers, by counting, into the right side of operational definitions. More precisely, the numeral occurs in the antecedent of the definiens, which states the so-called measuring procedure. The left side also contains this numeral which is being transferred there, if I may so express myself, by the definition. Let, in the case of length, the left side be 'x is of length three'. What is being counted are the layings-off mentioned on the right. In the case of time one counts the strokes of a pendulum; in the case of weight the unit weights in one pan of the balance; and so on. Actual measurement is in most cases much more complicated and indirect. But again, this does not at all detract from the clarifying power of the principle. Physical measurements, which are the most precise we can make, all rest on counting. In principle, this is all there is to the arithmetical side of these measurements, though, surely, it is not all there is to measurement. What it means for a measurement to be "precise," for instance, is itself a very neat question. I have said before that I do not intend to discuss now the logic of measurement. It will help, though, if I hint at the sort of thing that is involved. Two feet and$_1$ three feet make$_1$ five feet; two volumes N and$_2$ three volumes O make$_2$ (sometimes) two volumes N_2O_3. Yet '$2 + 3 = 5$' is a tautology and '$2 + 3 = 2$' is a contradiction. The point is that the two 'make' which I indexed have nothing whatsoever to do with logical identity ('$=$') and that the two indexed 'and' are quite different from '$+$' as well as from the logical 'and'. The latter two, by the way, '$+$' and 'and', though both logical, are also different from each other. We shall need these distinctions in the third chapter, in the analysis of configurations, when we shall probe the confusions of the Gestalt doctrine.

Rank orders are probably the best known and simplest instance of the other way in which numbers enter into synthetic statements. Assume that there are two descriptive relations, call them 'P' and 'E', such that for any two objects of a certain kind, call them 'a' and 'b', exactly one of the following three statements is true:

aPb, bPa, aEb.

If certain conditions are fulfilled, one can (in more than one way) to each object *a* assign a number, call it 'N*a*', so that '*aPb* if and only if N*a* < N*b*' and '*aEb* if and only if N*a* = N*b*' are both true. What makes this possible is, putting it roughly, certain similarities between '*P*' and '*E*', which name descriptive relations, on the one hand, and '<' and '=', which signify logical relations obtaining among numbers, on the other. Generally the idea is to assign numbers, or series of numbers, to things so that certain arithmetical relations obtain among the numbers assigned if and only if certain descriptive relations obtain among the things to which they are assigned. Some such "rules of assignment" are rather complicated. This is the other way in which numbers enter into synthetic statements or, what amounts to the same, in which concepts are quantified. In some measurements the two ways are combined.

The illustrations I used are all limited to the integers, 1, 2, 3, and so on. Yet we also employ fractions and even real numbers in measurement. Fractions can in principle be introduced "operationally," though, to be sure, a "reliable" measurement that yields more than a very few digits is in practice a major undertaking. But the use of real numbers that are not fractions, such as π and $\sqrt{2}$, goes definitely beyond the "operational basis." This raises some questions.

The only good reason for the use of real numbers is logical (arithmetical) convenience and simplicity. Not to use them is to deprive one's self of many useful patterns of inference, namely, all those corresponding to arithmetical tautologies in which real numbers that are not fractions occur. Using these actually simplifies computation (deductive inference). In some simple cases this is perhaps not readily apparent, e.g., when we want to compute the length of the diagonal of a square to three digits and, having measured its side with the same accuracy, consider the result of the measurement a real number, multiply this number by the real number $\sqrt{2}$ and then take the first three digits of the product. But when the "mathematics" involved is more complicated, the simplification is striking.

The use of real numbers in science does not rest on a "hypothesis," in the sense in which a law or a whole theory is a hypothesis. (A law is a synthetic generality and a theory is a whole class of laws!) To grasp this is particularly important now, when something else is becoming doubtful. That physical space-time in the subatomic realm is accurately represented by the continuum of four real-number coordinates (s,y,z,t) is indeed a hypothesis, in the sense in which a law is a hypothesis, though of course a much more encompassing one. It has long been taken for granted. Of late it has become doubtful. At least, it now makes scientific (not just philosophical) sense to question it (see p. 114).

But how are we to tie real numbers to the "operational basis"? The obvious way is through the partial interpretation of axiomatic calculi (p. 37). The operative word is 'partial'. Partiality, we saw, is the distinguishing characteristic of the procedure. Whenever we use real numbers we must thus assume that we have made some rather subtle coordinations by means of some rather complex rules between statements we understand on the one hand and those of an originally uninterpreted calculus on the other. But one must not be overimpressed with all this. If the use of real numbers were the only reason why operational definitions are sometimes inadequate, it would still be worth our while to inquire how far we could get with definitions alone if we relinquished the convenience of real numbers. In other words, one must try to bring out the differences between, say, length and a ψ-function rather than put them in the same boat for a reason that is fairly obvious. The real numbers are merely a part of the logical apparatus; concept formation is essentially a matter of the descriptive vocabulary. Thus it pays to put to one side the specific problems of the former in order to get an unencumbered view of the latter. To say the same thing differently, one had better assume that we start with the interpretation of an axiomatic calculus, so that real numbers are accommodated once and for all, and then ask how much can be done in this calculus by definitions alone.

So much for quantified concepts. Next, we must examine how, through them, arithmetic enters into the statement of a law. Take (1), $s = 16t^2$, the first of the three laws Galileo discovered. To begin with, this "equation" is not a tautology. ("Equations" that are, such as '$2 + 2 = 4$' and '$(a + b)^2 = a^2 + 2ab + b^2$' are, rather aptly, called identities.) What (1) states is a *functional connection* among the values of (in this case, two) quantified concepts, or, as one also says, among *variables*. More precisely, what is said is that if in certain situations (in this case, free fall) certain measurements are made (in this case, a time measure and the corresponding distance measure) and expressed in certain units, then the numbers obtained will, if substituted in the proper places of the formula, (approximately) yield an identity. Notice that I just said "what is said." The formula itself does not say it. This is always so. The formula is only a part of the statement of the law, comparable to the visible part of an iceberg. The definitions of the variables measured and the specification of the situations in which they are being measured are like the submerged part of the iceberg. To grasp this clearly, one merely has to consider that $y = 16x^2$ is just a parabola. The letters conventionally used, in this case 's' and 't', remind us of what we omit when the context permits.

Deduction from quantified laws is facilitated by the powerful patterns of inference arithmetic makes available. This, we saw, is one reason why quantification is so desirable. There is still another reason. To say it first quite informally, one cannot only *get* more from a quantified law, one already *has* more than in the case of a nonquantified generality whenever one knows such a law. This I must now explain. Then I shall have finished.

Simple examples are always helpful; in logical analysis they help even more if they are contrary to fact. Assume, then, that we know the tripartite law I mentioned before: every current$_1$ is also a current$_2$ and a current$_3$, and so on (p. 63). The law is, we remember, an adequate basis for a qualitative notion of (nonindexed) current. Assume, next, that we try to quantify this notion; either by means of the weight (i_1) of the precipitation out of a standard solution during a standard time interval; or by the size of the angle (i_2) of the deviation of a standard magnetic needle in a standard position; or by the amount of heat (i_3), by assumption already quantified, that develops in a standard wire during a standard time interval. Now we discover, and this is the contrary-to-fact feature of the story, that when the first "effect" is present in a certain quantity, say, i_1', the second and the third, while always present, still vary. Sometimes i_1' is associated with i_2' and i_3'; sometimes with i_2'' and i_3''; and so on. I need not further elaborate this imaginary story. We discovered, negatively, that the quantified notion of a (nonindexed) current "measured alternatively by any of these three effects" is not even consistent, let alone significant. Positively, we shall search for the variable or variables on which, given a value of i_1, the concomitant values of i_2 and i_3 still depend. How could we ever have found out all this without quantification, or, more precisely in the case of the story, without an attempt at quantification? This shows why, conversely, whenever we do know a quantified law, we know much more than if we only knew some related qualitative generality. Incidentally, the story corresponds quite accurately to a recent situation in psychology. Psychologists have for some time "measured" certain bits of behavior, say, a human eyelid reflex or an animal's pressing a bar, by what is known as amplitude (j_1), frequency (j_2), and latency (j_3). Quite often these measures were used alternatively. Yet psychologists have also constructed a theory according to which such bits of behavior depend on a single (though highly defined) variable, the so-called effective excitatory potential (E), which has also been quantified. This makes sense only if (1) each value E' of E corresponds to one and only one triple (j_1', j_2', j_3',), and (2) each of the three values in such a triple determines uniquely the two others. Happily, the leading behavior theorists are by now fully aware of this sort of thing.

I promised to dispose at the end of the confusion caused by some philosophical uses of 'quantity' and 'quality'. Experience is qualitative; science is quantitative; the gulf is unbridgeable. Or, in a slightly less radical version, since experience is qualitative, the methods of the quantitative disciplines must of necessity fail in psychology. We have all heard the words. I do not know what they mean. Rather, I know that they make no sense. Every undefined descriptive concept is "qualitative." The definition of every defined descriptive concept contains therefore at least one "qualitative" term. The definitions of some concepts also contain numbers. Such concepts are called "quantitative." I know no other intelligible meanings of 'qualitative' and 'quantitative'. It follows that, if one insists on using the two words, one must say that every descriptive term is fundamentally "qualitative" and that the use of numerals in synthetic statements is merely a logical elaboration of "quality." Yet the analysis that leads me to this conclusion is unmistakably of the kind the worried defenders of "quality" reject as in principle inadequate because it is, among other things, oriented toward the "quantitative." Is there a better and simpler way to convince one's self that the shouting is about nothing?

CHAPTER TWO

Process and history

DESCRIPTION AND EXPLANATION

SEEING a pot of water that is being heated over a fire, I say (1) 'This is water' and (2) 'This is being heated'. After a while, seeing what I see, I add (3) 'This (water) boils'. Knowing what I know, when I made the first two statements I could have added 'This will boil'. But let us assume that I waited until I had occasion to assert (3). This permits me to disregard for the time being the temporal sequence. To simplify still further, assume that all I mean by a thing being heated and by a thing boiling is, in the first case, that it is close to a flame and, in the second, the characteristic movement, bubbling, and noise. (1), (2), and (3) state what I "see"; they are, as I shall say, a *description* of individual facts. Assume next that, while the water is boiling, I am asked (4) 'Why does this (water) boil?' I may answer either (5) 'Water if heated boils' or (5a) 'It boils because it is being heated'. If asked (4a) 'What is the cause of this (water) boiling?' I am perhaps more likely to answer by (5a) than by (5). Presently we shall see that there is no difference either between the two questions or between the two answers. Strictly speaking, neither of the latter is very satisfactory. 'Because it has been heated sufficiently to come to a boil under the prevailing atmospheric pressure' would be more accurate. I am not at the moment concerned with this sort of accuracy; so I shall stay with the simpler answers. To ask a question that begins with 'why' or to ask for the cause of something is to ask for an *explanation*. An explanation of an individual fact consists in its identification as (a part of) an instance of a law. This is explicit in the variant (4), (5); it is merely implicit in the variant (4a), (5a); so I shall first examine the former. (5) states the law involved; because I spoke as we ordinarily do, it does not contain either 'all' or 'every' or 'any'. Fully expanded, (5) reads 'Every sample of water if heated boils'. One is tempted to make this statement even more complete by adding 'at any time, at any place, under all circumstances'. A little reflection shows that one wouldn't have added anything. If a circumstance isn't mentioned in a law or, for that matter, in any statement, then the latter says—by omission—that the former is irrelevant to the truth of what it does say. (Otherwise we could never manage to say anything.) Some people do sometimes speak of "conditions" under which a law holds. This is really very misleading. The statement of those "conditions" is a part of the law; specifically, it is a part of its antecedent. Practically, one need not always bother to state all the "conditions" we know to be relevant. Literally, we assert on such occasions something we know to be a falsehood or, as one also says, again so misleadingly, a "law" that has "exceptions," namely, those cases in which the "condition" is not fulfilled. Conversely, a circumstance may be relevant without our knowing it, so that we do not mention it even when we state as accurately as we can what we believe to be a true generality and yet, because of this omission, is a falsehood. This is just one facet of the ubiquitous hazards of induction to which the most firmly established law of physics is in principle no less subject than the most tentative hypothesis of a social scientist. But all this is really quite obvious.

(5) explains (3). It is an explanation because

> (1) This is water
> (2) This is being heated
> (5) Water if heated boils
> ―――――――――――――――
> (3) This boils

is a valid argument. This is the heart of the matter. It also shows why I just said that what is explained is a part of what is identified as an instance of a law. In our example, the instance is stated by (1), (2), and (3). The part that is being explained, in this case (3), which is also called the "effect," appears in the conclusion. The remaining part, in this case (1) and (2), also called the "cause," appears among the premises. We understand now why (4) and (5) amount to the same thing as (4a) and (5a). The only difference is that (5) mentions explicitly the law that occurs among the premises; (5a) states explicitly the other premises. But the understanding is, in either case, that there is a valid argument of this kind. It follows that 'cause' and its derivatives and cognates, such as 'because', are expendable. They can be expurgated from an improved language. Since 'cause' has been put to many "philosophical" uses, this is both enlightening and important. Its nonphilosophical use, which is often convenient, is governed by many subtle cues. One tends to speak of causes and effects only if the laws involved have certain features. For our purposes all this belongs in small print. But first for one more comment on 'explanation'. The way I introduced it, what is being explained is always an individual fact. This is a bit narrow. The term is often without harmful ambiguity used more broadly. Consider a theory, say, Newtonian mechanics. If its axioms are combined with the description of the solar system at a certain moment, Kepler's laws follow deductively. The similarity to our original illustration is apparent. So it is quite reasonable to say, as one does, that Newton explained the laws Kepler discovered.

If it were not expendable, 'cause' would have to be counted as a nonlogical word. Readers of the small print will recognize the connection with what I said earlier (p. 62) about the philosophical uses of 'power' and 'disposition'. If these three words, 'cause', 'power', and 'disposition', named anything, that is, if they had to be included among the descriptive words of an improved language, the things named would be very much of a kind. Accordingly, 'because' could, like the subjunctive, be used to mark in the statement itself the difference between a "genuine" law of nature and an "incidental" generality. To drag in once more the bench on which "as it happened" only Irishmen sat, we reject 'For every x: x is an Irishman *because* x sat on it' as false even though the corresponding indicative generality, 'For every x: if x sat on it then x is an Irishman', be true.

Take (a) 'Everything green is extended' and (b) 'If two angles of a triangle are 40° and 60° respectively then the third is 80°'. If we speak as the tongue runs, we do not say that something being green is the cause of its being extended or that two angles of a triangle being 40° and 60° respectively is the cause of the third being 80°. Yet both (a) and (b) are synthetic generalities or laws. In the case of (b) this is obvious, at least if it is understood as I meant it, namely, as a statement about triangles, not as a proposition from some uninterpreted calculus. The only thing peculiar about (a) is its simplicity. As we ordinarily speak and think of laws, particularly when we discuss science, we do not think of anything quite as self-evident and familiar. But there is no difference in principle. To convince one's self that (a) is synthetic, one merely has to replace the two character words by two others, say 'blue' and 'hot'. 'Everything blue is hot' is not even true. Yet we know that in a tautology all descriptive words occur vacuously. The reason for our not speaking in either case of "causes" and "effects" is probably the absence of any reference to time, either explicitly or, as in our example of the boiling pot of water, implicitly. We shall have occasion to discuss such "noncausal" or, as I would rather say, cross-sectional laws later on.

When I am asked why I have a cold I must sometimes truthfully answer that I walked in the rain without a hat, as I like to do, though I am bald. In this case the law is apparently taken for granted and what is referred to as the cause is a particular fact. This is not so when we say that the "attraction" of the moon is the cause of the tides or that slackening investment is among the causes of unemployment. In these cases the reference is to a law. But the ambiguity is as harmless as it is obvious. Let me give two examples of the subtler uses of 'cause'.

1. We say that the perturbations of the orbits of the planets, that is, their rather slight deviations from ellipses, are caused by their mutual attraction. What that means is this. If in computing the orbits from Newton's laws we proceed as if the planets did not attract each other, we obtain elliptic orbits. If we take the mutual attraction of the planets into account, we find (a) that the orbits we obtain are not very different from the ellipses I just mentioned, and (b) that the computation proceeds in a manner properly described as a solution by successive approximations, of which those ellipses are the first step.

2. Some readers who thought, unwisely, that my story of the three currents was childish may have muttered to themselves that the true or real "cause" of the three (and all other) "effects" of electric currents is certain movements of the electrons in the wire. At this use of 'cause' I have hinted before (p.

66). There is a very complex theory containing whole chains of deductions by which laws are, in the broader sense of 'explaining', explained by others that can in turn be explained. In this hierarchy certain laws about movements of electrons in a wire stand high above those that state what a wire connected with the poles of a galvanic battery does to a magnetic needle. In this sense of 'cause', the real or true cause, or an "alternative cause," or a "partial cause," of my cold was not that I walked bald and bareheaded in the rain but, probably, what a sudden drop in temperature did to certain nerves in my head.

The phrases 'alternative cause' and 'partial cause' are just two from a whole battery invented to express in the logically clumsy terminology of cause and effect (one cause-one effect!) what can be said more easily and more clearly without it. Some subtle differences in the use of 'cause', 'condition', and 'factor' serve the same purpose. This will become clear as I proceed though I shall not take time to point it out. On the other hand, I shall make no effort to avoid the cause-effect terminology. Our language is so constituted that what is logically clumsy is often idiomatically very convenient.

Some readers may be confused by the several uses to which I put 'descriptive'. A little glossary is therefore in order. (a) The word is used as the name of a kind of words. The dichotomy is: logical-descriptive. (b) The word occurs in the inseparable phrase 'definite description'. The dichotomy is: proper name-descriptive phrase. (c) Descriptions, as I now speak of them, are *statements* of individual fact (not either words or phrases). I have not finished discussing this matter, but the relevant contrasts are, obviously, "explanation" and "law." All these uses are traditional and I am reluctant to coin new terms. There is still another thing that may have puzzled some. "Science does not explain, it merely describes" is a familiar formula of the tradition within which my analysis stands. Yet I distinguish between description and explanation and insist that science explains. The formula, glittering and in need of explication like all such formulae, stands traditionally for three things. (1) It asserts a Humean conception of causality—no causes, no powers, no dispositions, in the "philosophical" uses of these terms. (2) All explanation must come to an end. Statements of individual fact are explained by laws; laws are explained by theories; every theory has axioms; no theory can explain its own axioms. (3) Explanation need not and does not produce understanding, or less ambiguously, "empathic understanding." With this latter notion we shall deal in Volume Two.

One more point. I am simplifying the exposition by often speaking as if all-statements were the only kind of generality. Practically this will do no harm; technically it is false. There-are-statements are the other kind of generality. To grasp the logical connection between the two, one merely has to remember that 'all' and 'some' can be defined in terms of each other with the help of 'not' (p. 46); and there is also a connection with respect to induction. A (synthetic) all-statement cannot be conclusively verified by any finite number of instances, though it can be falsified by a single counterinstance. A (synthetic) there-are-statement cannot be conclusively falsified by any number of counterinstances, though it can be verified by a single positive instance. This shows both the similarities and the differences.

Science explains by laws what the scientist first describes by statements of individual fact. This is fundamental. It entails that if one's prediction, the description of the future effect, does not agree with what he eventually sees, he must change his ideas about what the law is, not about what the individual facts are. The distinction between statements of law and of individual fact or, what amounts to the same thing, between explanation and description must thus be clear-cut and well grounded. In principle it is. In principle, description precedes and is independent of explanation. For description tells us *what* is there, explanation *why* it is there. To me this is evident. Yet we shall do well to examine carefully the arguments of those who deny, in principle, the distinction; particularly since their arguments are part and parcel of a powerful intellectual tradition. The reason for unravelling them here is that in this very form, the alleged inseparability of the "what" and the "why," they were among the most prominent and, at the time, effective arguments in the barrage the early Functionalists directed against classical psychology. Their pattern is Hegelian. So it is not surprising that, as we shall see in Volume Three, the Functionalists derived their inspiration, in this respect as in some others, from Hegel's intellectual heir, John Dewey.

In the example I used the prediction came true, the water boiled. Consider now a story without such a happy ending. I look at a certain object, notice its color and characteristically irregular shape, touch it and try to knead it, smell it, perhaps, and say 'This is (a piece of) wax'. Since I know that wax if (sufficiently) heated melts, I predict that this object will melt if it is held over a flame. There is no need to go into details once more. My prediction is put to the test. The object does not melt; or it does not melt as easily as wax would; this sort of accuracy is again beside the point. I decide that 'This is wax' is false; I do not decide that 'Wax if heated melts' is false. Further investigation reveals that both decisions were sound. Chemical tests show that the object in question consists of one of those substances chemists know how to synthesize, which are in many respects like others, in this case like wax, without however having some of their properties, because they are less useful for some purpose, in this case without the low melting point of wax.

What is the point of this simple story? Here is what the rationalist says. "Notice that you did not permit the outcome of an experiment to refute a law. Faced with the choice between the truth of either 'This is wax' or 'Wax if heated melts', you sacrificed not the law but what you insist on calling the statement of individual fact. What happened in this case can, in principle, happen *in all cases*. This destroys, in principle, the value of your distinction between the what and the why; since if it means anything at all, it means that there is a class of statements, those you call statements of individual fact, whose truth always takes precedence in choices of the kind your second story illustrates. I conclude, therefore, that your (statements of) individual facts are a myth." At first sight the argument is impressive. Surely it requires an answer. But let me first identify the pattern it follows. Since I let the rationalist have the first word, I think I deserve this compensatory advantage. If a law cannot, in principle, be refuted by an experiment, then it becomes, after a fashion, the definition, or a part of the definition, of the terms that occur in it. (There is even a technical name for this confused idea. The phrase is 'implicit definition'.) For instance, wax if heated melts, by definition; this, though heated, does not melt; hence this is not wax. Since definitions are analytic, we recognize again the rationalist tendency to enlarge the domain of the analytic, which is as it were the mind's province, at the expense of the synthetic or factual. In order to satisfy this need the idealists among the rationalists sacrifice, in this particular kind of argument, the self-containedness of individual fact. The word that comes to mind is "holism." In Volume Three we shall see that this is indeed the exact point of contact between the Gestalt doctrine and the Hegelian tradition. In the English-speaking countries the idealistic line leads from Hegel over the British Idealists to Dewey.

The defense of the distinction between description and explanation starts from the phrase I underlined in the rationalist's speech: *in all cases.* In the case of my story, which I chose deliberately in order to give the rationalist a run for his money, he is of course right. The abandonment of 'This is wax' turns out to be "warranted." (This is Dewey's word. An instrumentalist must not use 'true'.) But this is not so in all cases. It has been said, very aptly I think, that all bad philosophy stems from good arguments pushed too far, by a fallacious transition to the limit, as it were. I shall arrange the analysis of the holistic fallacy in three steps, one paragraph to each step.

1. *Practically,* we know that it is not safe in this age of chemistry to take such statements as 'This is wax' for granted after only a few observations made by our unaided senses. But we also know that, practically, we shall never have to retract certain other assertions, namely, those which describe what we see by means of atomic statements of the "realistic" language. These are, to refresh our memory, the statements that contain, aside from the expendable 'is', no logical words and only undefined descriptive words of that language; for instance, 'This is to the left of that', said about two chairs, or 'this is hard', said upon touching a stone. Practically, such assertions are completely self-contained; nothing I know in addition to what they state when I make them or which I may come to know in the future is of even the slightest relevance to their truth. Incidentally, this is

one of the reasons why a "realistic" language is an adequate tool of analysis in the philosophy of science.

2. *In principle,* I might have dreamt that I saw the chairs and touched the stone. I need not retell this old tale that was first told by Descartes. What happened, not surprisingly, in the case of the piece of wax, could, in principle though rather surprisingly, also happen in the case of assertions made by atomic statements of a "realistic" language. It could not happen, not even in principle, with respect to the atomic statements of a "phenomenalistic" language, that is, we remember, of a language whose undefined descriptive predicates refer to characters of mental contents. In principle, the only statements of individual fact are therefore the atomic statements of a "phenomenalistic" language. But this suffices to establish the distinction between description and explanation, between the what and the why, in principle. In other words, the assertions we make when we describe, as one says, the stream of consciousness by means of atomic statements of a "phenomenalistic" language are incorrigible. When I "see" pink mice in the corner of my study, I shall, after I have recovered from whatever ailed me, soon come to know that there were no pink mice and that I have suffered from a hallucination. But this has not the slightest tendency to throw any doubt on the truth of such atomic statements of a "phenomenalistic" language as I might have used to describe my mental contents as I had them. ('This is a mouse', as we ordinarily use it, is of course not an atomic statement of such a language. 'This is a mouse-percept' gives the idea. It is still much too complex, though, and the 'percept' in 'mouse-percept', which I had to add for identification since we do not actually have a working language of this sort, is misleading.)

3. *Practically,* when we test one law, we take some others for granted. *In principle,* we never test one law in isolation. Take an astronomical observation. It "involves," at least, the laws of optics as well as those of celestial mechanics. If the result is not what we expected it to be we can therefore, in principle, modify either the laws of optics or those of celestial mechanics. I shall not examine the freedom we have in this respect; but it is well worth an accurate analysis since, though it has limitations, it is much greater than one might think. To take advantage of it leads once in a great while to theoretical advance. But notice that the choice is always among generalities, never among laws on the one hand and statements of individual fact on the other. If we had "in all cases" a choice of this latter kind, then we could never know how to choose. This is, to me, the most telling argument of all. That is why I left it to the end. Consider again the case of the piece of wax. (For convenience sake and as I practically can, I speak "realistically," though in principle I could and should speak "phenomenalistically.") On what grounds did I "choose" to consider 'Wax if heated melts' rather than 'This is wax' as the true statement? I saw that the object

did not melt. But then I must have known, because of what I saw, that 'This does not melt' is true! The holist who is prepared for this objection admits that we do indeed not know the truth of 'This does not melt' either; only, he observes that if we take it rather than 'This is wax' to be "warranted," then our statements will "fit" better. This is his criterion of choice. I merely ask: fit with *what?* What else could they conceivably be fitted to than to what I see because it is self-containedly there for me to see when I make the fit? If, on the other hand, all that is meant is that the several statements we choose—though I can on this account not see why we should assert any of them—fit better with each other, in the sense that they do not contradict each other, then the refutation proceeds as follows. If a class of statements taken together leads to a contradiction, then at least one of them must indeed be false. The converse does not hold. The mistaken identification of consistency (the technical term they used was 'coherence') with factual truth is indeed characteristic of the idealistic variant of rationalism. Yet the consistency of a class of statements has, *in principle,* not the slightest tendency to warrant the assertion of any of its members. *Practically,* there is again no disagreement. Nobody doubts that if the head of a laboratory receives repeatedly from an inexperienced worker observation reports that do not jibe with established laws, he will be well advised to question the competence or the diligence of the worker rather than those laws. Even so, the neophyte could be right.

I conclude that the distinction between the what and the why is well grounded. This insight will stand us in good stead in the analysis of Gestalt, in that of Functionalism, and in our own efforts at clarification. In conclusion, I shall secure it with an example from psychological practice. A clinician reads in a reliable report that the patient he is examining has during a certain time interval with a certain frequency on certain occasions exhibited certain kinds of behavior. The report contains the statements of individual fact in the case and nothing else. On it the clinician bases his diagnosis. According to the (actually not yet existing) precise definition of a certain mental disease the patient suffers from this disease. A year later the clinician learns that after the man left his consultation room he never again behaved in those ways even though the occasions which previously elicited the critical behavior continued to occur. If the clinician knows a (statistical) law according to which sufferers from the disease either have lucid intervals or are sometimes cured in a single session, then he has no problem. If the accepted laws exclude these possibilities, then he has a problem and a choice. He will either reject the laws or "change his diagnosis." The first alternative is clear; the wording of the second requires some explication. Our clinician may think that there is a symptom, which he hopes to discover, such that if the patient had shown it in addition to those on which the original diagnosis was based, he would not either have had a lucid interval or been cured in one session. What he does or, rather, what he hopes to do after he has discovered that symptom is, therefore, to propose two new definitions (syndromes). For the new syndrome, which includes the new symptom in addition to the old ones, he keeps the old word, largely because he thinks that with this new meaning the accepted laws in which the old word occurs are true. For the old syndrome he invents a new name. The analogy with the piece of wax and the synthetic substance I mistook for wax is obvious. Nor is there any doubt that at the present state of knowledge the story is quite realistic. This is one reason why I spent so much time on the piece of wax. We are all too easily tempted to comfort ourselves for the simple absence of knowledge with philosophies that blur the firm outlines of individual fact.

One might think that the explication I gave of 'individual fact' is purely syntactical: an individual fact is what is referred to by an atomic statement. This is not so; the notion of a "phenomenalistic" language that we had to introduce into the analysis is not a purely syntactical notion. In other words, the only foolproof notion of individual fact is what is referred to by the "simplest" statements of an otherwise improved language whose undefined descriptive words name the "simplest" things we know (concerning 'simple', see p. 41). Technically, it amounts to this. Assume that 'This is a mouse' is atomic in the "realistic" language. (One could easily define 'mouse' in such a language; but the difference makes no difference.) The statement that corresponds to it, even most schematically, in a "phenomenalistic" language is anything but atomic; it contains many 'all' and 'some'. The "uncertainty" of 'This is a mouse' is therefore just another instance of the pervasive "uncertainty" of induction, though admittedly an abstruse one and of interest only to the logical analyst.

Certainty, as I said before (p. 28), is a character of beliefs, not of their contents. Any other use of the word and its cognates is therefore dispensable, may cause confusion, and needs explication. One such use I explicated before: (a) what is "certain" is what is analytic. In this section I explicated two others. (b) If a statement is formed from another by generalization, then the former is less "certain" than the latter in that no finite number of premises like the latter allows deduction of the generalization. This is, so to speak, a relative notion of certainty. Tracing it as far as we can, we arrive at (c): "certain" is what is described by an atomic statement of the "phenomenalistic" language. An unanalyzed notion of certainty is probably an ingredient of the unanalyzed notion of direct acquaintance. Historically, it probably accounts in part for the philosophers' desire to "start" from mental contents. But this search for certainty has also done much harm, partly because the notion is, as we see, very ambiguous, partly because it has obscured the essentially descriptive nature of the analytical enterprise by lending aid and comfort to the elusive idea of "presuppositionless" philosophizing.

The new rationalists make much of the "uncertainty" of "all" knowledge. They believe it guarantees that plasticity of the world which they metaphysically exaggerate so that man can play his metaphysically exaggerated role in it, bringing about "progress." The classical rationalists, on the other hand, whose thought patterns they inherit, insist that we know at least some laws by reason alone and, therefore, for certain. Grasping both these points firmly helps one to understand both the dilemma of the new rationalists and the way they solved it. They sacrifice not only the "certainty" of individual facts: they sacrifice these facts altogether. In the ideal limit laws become definitions. In this they follow Hegel. Science advances by juggling its definitions to approach the limit ever more closely. In this they combine Aristotle (p. 53) with the idea of "progress."

THE PARADIGM: CELESTIAL MECHANICS

In the remainder of this book, the rest of this chapter as well as the next, I shall examine various aspects of explanation. For good reasons I shall in all these explications use the same example. In this section I shall first state these reasons and then with some care describe the paradigm itself, the Newtonian mechanics of mass points or, what amounts to the same thing, prerelativistic celestial mechanics.

Take (1) 'Water if heated boils' and (2) 'Near the surface of the earth a stone if deprived of support moves downward (falls)'. Being laws, both statements can be used in genuine explanations. Yet each states merely a piece of very imperfect knowledge. For one thing, they are both qualitative in areas in which quantification has been very successful. For another, they both neglect factors, in (1) pressure, in (2) air resistance and exact distance from the earth's center of gravity, that are relevant and under some circumstances produce "exceptions." Nor is this all I mean by calling (1) and (2) *imperfect* bits of knowledge (imperfect laws). Take, on the other hand, (3) the axioms of thermodynamics or (4) those of Newtonian mechanics. They are examples of knowledge that is, in a sense, *perfect*. Of course, I shall have to explain this use of 'perfect' and 'imperfect'. I hold no special brief for these two words. I chose them because I had to choose some and because they will probably do as well as any other pair. ('Complete' and 'incomplete' I reserve for a later occasion.) As with any ordinary word made into a technical term, one must beware of confusing associations. Here are two respects in which no piece of knowledge is ever "perfect." For one thing, every quantified statement is subject to the limitations of measurement which, though we decided to ignore them, are a worthy object of detailed logical analysis. For another, no law can ever escape the "uncertainty" of induction. The theory of relativity, for instance, has reduced (4) to the status of an approximation, though one so accurate that in all but a few very special cases the difference cannot be measured.

Up to now, all examples were of the imperfect kind. To produce some understanding of the other kind, the one I call perfect, one can proceed in either of two ways. One can, so to speak, work up gradually from the former to the latter. This alternative retraces the actual process of discovery; for perfect knowledge, even though not "perfect" in a foolish sense, is not come by without long and laborious accumulation of imperfect knowledge. The other alternative, the one I chose, is to introduce abruptly and to analyze directly a specimen of perfect knowledge. It has, I believe, two major advantages. *First.* The imperfect laws of an area (which may be practically quite adequate for many purposes) follow deductively from the law or laws that constitute perfect knowledge in the area. Since this is so, helpful distinctions among kinds of imperfect knowledge will flow automatically from a closer analysis of how such items fit into the schema of knowledge that is perfect. *Second.* All philosophical ideas are best clarified by means of "schemata." Nor is that a matter of chance; for that is where they stem from. They are merely a way of making explicit what is implicit in the schemata which, whether we know it or not, guide our thought. Confusion arises only if one identifies the schema with the world or, which is really not much different, if one feels bound to argue that the latter must in every detail conform to the former. I used this method, clarification by means of schemata, when I introduced the notion of an improved language; in a sense I am always using it since my whole conception of philosophical analysis rests on it. Specifically, we saw that the dichotomies analytic-synthetic and logical-descriptive are clear-cut only in an artificial language or schema. But if and only if one has understood them there, can one analyze the questions that center around the "philosophical" meanings of these words. Now I shall make another specific use of the method, though on a much more modest scale. This time Newton's laws of celestial mechanics will serve as my schema. I know of no better way to clarify our ideas about what science is, what it is not, and what it would be in the ideal limit, than to examine this particular specimen of perfect knowledge. Surely, there are other such specimens; for instance, classical thermodynamics or the theory of Faraday and Maxwell. I have some additional reasons for choosing celestial mechanics.

Third. Celestial mechanics was the actual source of, or, perhaps better, the most potent single stimulus for the ideas it can be used to explicate. Not only was it historically the first spectacular success of modern science; whether they knew it or not, it has ever since moulded the scientists' ideas about what science is or ought to be. Nor were the philosophers less impressed. To mention just one rather trivial though revealing circumstance, had Newton's achievement not been in the area of mechanics, the word 'mechanistic' would never have been put to any of its several "philosophical" uses. For our purposes and from where I stand, the purely historical importance of our paradigm is admittedly a minor advantage. But it is not to be despised and it falls into our lap for nothing, as it were. *Fourth.* Of all specimens of perfect knowledge Newtonian mechanics is the simplest I know. It is quantified, of course; so I shall be able to use, quite realistically, the conventional x's and f's, without and with subscripts and superscripts, in speaking about its variables, their functional connections, and their values. This makes for the lucidity and manageability of a schema. But our paradigm is also simple in a sense in which not all quantified theories are simple. The relative complexity of its structure makes it an excellent specimen of the finer structure of theories. But again, it is the "simplest" instance of this "complexity," so simple indeed that it can without violence be looked at as a single law, or as a class of very "similar" laws with an increasing number of parameters. This is the way I shall for the most part look at it in this chapter. In the next chapter I shall examine it as a theory.

Fifth. One may wonder why I haven't, in spite of all these virtues of my paradigm, taken one from the behavior sciences. I would have done just that if there were one that is formally as articulate and has stood up materially as long and as well. There are, I believe, some specimens in contemporary economic theory. But though quite full-blown in form, materially they are still rather frail and controversial. Nor do I master them sufficiently to trust myself with them. In psychology the one candidate is modern behavior theory; but it is not as well articulated in form and it also has some other peculiarities which make it seem wiser to consider it in the light of Newtonian perfection. I shall do that in Volume Two. The situation is by no means a matter of chance. If there were in the behavior sciences a specimen of perfect knowledge materially as successful as Newtonian mechanics, certain questions about these sciences would no longer be asked. (Not that they need not be answered; otherwise I wouldn't bother with them at all; even so, I bother as little as I responsibly can. But if we knew more about behavior, their interest would be largely historical. The Paduan Aristotelians (p. 67) virtually lost their audience after Newton.) In a sense, then, I am making a virtue out of a necessity by choosing my paradigm as I do. However, there is more to this choice. Perhaps the most effective way in which a logical analyst refutes his critics is by showing that certain features (of the world, or of our experience, or of science) which according to the critics can be accounted for only if one accepts their, the critics', analysis, can in fact be accommodated within the analysis criticized. Now it is still argued that the behavior sciences must not adopt the "logic" of the physical sciences, since the latter, being "mechanistic," could not possibly provide all those subtler patterns needed in the former. And then we are usually given a list of such patterns. To be shown accurately that even Newtonian "mechanics" has room for all of them is a poignant lesson. I am saying this once and for all and I shall not waste my breath by blowing this horn on all the proper occasions. Yet I recommend these two points, the general one about the analyst's technic of refutation and the more specific one about the alleged limitations of physical science, as proper subjects for meditation.

Notice that though I shall use a schema of x's and f's, this "symbolism" is not that of "symbolic logic" or artificial languages but that of ordinary nonformalized arithmetic, which is in principle a part of ordinary language. Perusing psychological journals as I do, I must say, in the psychologists' jargon, that logical symbols in them have acquired a very high cue value for me. I turn the page.

The "simplicity" of Newtonian mechanics disappears if it is subjected to the probing that led to the theory of relativity. Let me say, then, that I shall throughout treat time and space prerelativistically. For my purposes anything else would be sheer window dressing. This leads to another comment.

There is now and there has been for about a generation a good deal of talk, in the nether regions of the intellectual universe, to the effect that in the two great revolutions of this century, relativity and quantum mechanics, physics itself has shed the "mechanistic" and "deterministic" strait jacket of Newtonian "mechanics." Every thoughtful contemporary knows how ambiguous and, because of its essential anti-intellectualism, dangerous this "line" is, even though it is sometimes with the best of intentions used in futile attempts to defend attitudes one might share. That sort of thing is not my concern in this book. It is worth mentioning, though, that these views are also thoroughly mistaken, some Sunday philosophers who happen to be eminent scientists during the week to the contrary notwithstanding. Aside from the problems that arise in the analysis of space and time, the theory of relativity, epochal as it is in physics, is even in the philosophy of physics a mere matter of detail. Aside from the technical treatment of time, it is in its form and even in its first appearance, if I may so express myself, Newtonian. In quantum mechanics the occurrence of "statistical" lawfulness on a "very fundamental" level of the theory produces at least the appearance of a "fundamental" discrepancy. The appearance is deceptive. The "most fundamental" level of the theory or, to use a word of which I seem to be fond, the "schema" of quantum mechanics is Newtonian. Technically, the second Schroedinger equation is a differential equation in time. But of this in some later small print (p. 124). Quite nontechnically again, nobody has as yet devised an articulate schema fundamentally different from Newton's that either with scientists or with philosophers could pass for that of scientific explanation. So profound was the impact of this great man. But of course he stood, like all great men, on the shoulders of great predecessors, most eminently Galileo and Descartes.

Now for the paradigm. Consider a number of celestial bodies, say, ten, sufficiently close to each other to affect appreciably each other's motion, sufficiently far away from all others not to be so affected by them. Our planetary system is very nearly such a "system." Its description consists of ten statements of individual fact, each specifying the mass of one of the bodies. I shall schematically represent it by $[m_1, m_2, \ldots\ldots, m_{10}]$, the ordered series of the ten numbers each of which occurs in one and only one of the ten statements.* Schematically, each body is considered to be an unextended point. The practical success of this idealization is due to the fact that the dimensions of these bodies, huge as they are compared with ourselves, are yet negligible compared with their mutual distances. (Nothing is either large or small in itself. Accordingly, what is impressive about a measurement is not the number of zeros that either follows the last or precedes the first of the digits other than zero but, rather, the number of places between the former and the latter.) No prediction can be made from the description of the system alone. What we predict is one "state" of the system from another. A "state" is a state of the system at a given moment. Its description, too, consists of a number of statements of individual fact. In our case, it consists of twenty such statements, two for each body, one specifying its position, one specifying its velocity at the moment. If one represents, as one usually does, each position and each speed by its components along three Cartesian axes, the count runs up to sixty statements of individual fact. This is really the more reasonable way of counting. So I shall, in our case, represent a state description by $[x_1{}^{t_1}, x_2{}^{t_1}, \ldots \ldots \ldots ,$ $x_{60}{}^{t_1}]$, an ordered series of sixty numbers, each of which occurs in one and only one of the sixty statements. The ordinary way of writing them, x, y, z, $\dot{x}$, $\dot{y}$, $\dot{z}$, with subscripts from 1 to 10, though very convenient for computational purposes, blurs the basic logic of the schema. The x's without superscripts are variables; x_{14}, for instance, stands for the second position coordinate of the fourth body, the one with mass m_4. The superscript indicates the time moment by the reading of some standard clock. $x_{14}{}^{t_1}$ is thus not a variable but a number, the value of the variable x_{14} at the moment t_1. Sometimes I shall write C (from 'configuration') for the description of the system; S^t, for the description of its state at time t. The law is an equation (more precisely, in this case, thirty statements of functional connection) that permits the computation, for every value of t, say, t_2, of S^{t_2} from S^{t_1} and C; diagrammatically:

$$(C \ \& \ S^{t_1}) \longrightarrow S^{t_2}.$$

For $t_2 < t_1$, our prediction is thus really postdiction. There is no harm in applying to all cases of explanation a term that fits literally only the most interesting one. Besides, one might say that a law always predicts from what we know at the moment what is as yet unknown, whether it lies in the future or whether we have not inspected it though it lies in the present or whether we would have to look it up in a record of the past.

Calling the sixty propositions making up our S statements of individual fact involves a good deal of schematization or idealization. Having meas-

---

*Since there is here no danger of ambiguity, I am not fussing with semantical quotes. For instance, I just wrote $[m_1, m_2, \ldots \ldots , m_{10}]$; not, as I strictly should, '$[m_1, m_2, \ldots \ldots , m_{10}]$'.

ured the length of a ledge with a yardstick and then stating the result, we assert what is literally, except for some philosophical purposes, a statement of individual fact. But we do not climb some heavenly scaffold, armed with some heavenly yardstick to lay off on the mutual distances of the heavenly bodies. The simplification I thus permit myself does not omit or blur anything essential. Mass and velocity require some attention. The concept of mass must be defined. Of this presently, in small print. Velocity forces us to take time seriously. So far I have, quite deliberately, dodged closer consideration of this all-important variable. Now three comments are in order.

1. Literally, there are no mathematical moments of time, just as there are no mathematical points in space. In other words, we are not acquainted with anything and we cannot, in the literal sense of definition, define anything to which we can coordinate accurately a single real number rather than an interval, however minute, on a "time line" of real numbers.

To make such coordinations which are, as we saw, nevertheless most useful, one must, as we also saw, resort to the interpretation of axiomatic systems. The usefulness of such axiomatizations of space and time may have its limits (p. 71).

2. Half of the statements in a state description specify velocities, that is, rates of change of position *at a moment*. Technically, velocities are limits, in the sense of the differential calculus, of speeds during small intervals. The dialectic of moments extends therefore to velocities; for our purposes it belongs in small print. Conversely, if one does use real numbers in the Newtonian fashion then the only correct way to think of velocities is as momentary. This is one reason why I am counting the variables through, in the special case from 1 to 60.

The as yet very confused situation in quantum mechanics suggests strongly that even if we should give up the notion of a real-number-space-time-continuum (I express myself rather concisely), we would still not give up the notion of "velocities" at whatever would then in the axiomatic system take the place of a "moment." This is the hard core of the notion of conjugate coordinates in quantum mechanics.

3. The most striking feature of Newtonian lawfulness and one of the major sources of its power is that, skipping the intermediate states, it permits the computation of all states, that is, of the state at any moment, from that at one moment. This is very remarkable and has nothing whatsoever to do with the issue of real numbers which outside of the logic of quanta is a mere technicality. The source of this remarkable power lies in the structure of the equations that state the functional connections. The point is that some variables in these equations are, by definition, the rates of change of the others. (Technically, this means that the equations are differential equations in time.) This form is not only extremely lucid in itself

but also invites the use of powerful arithmetical tools. The laws of current behavior theory are not of this form. This is a large part of what I meant when I said that in them the Newtonian form is not fully articulated. (The other part is, as we shall presently see, their historicity.) That does not mean that one cannot force them into this form. One can always play mathematical games, just as one can wear boots too large for the size of one's feet. I see not much point in either. The most such mathematical tricks can show is brought out much more clearly and less pretentiously by the sort of logical analysis I am attempting, since it forces our attention, rather than distracting it, on both the similarities and the differences and on what is and what is not essential in them.

In what follows I mention instead of the quantified concepts themselves the variables for which we substitute their values. That one can do this is one of the conveniences of a quantified schema.

The basic vocabulary of the theory (p. 32) is the x's, t, and the m's. Since velocities are defined in terms of positions and time, one can even limit one's self to the position x's. As one usually says, the basic concepts of Newtonian mechanics are spatial, temporal, and in addition, mass.

Newton's theory began, like all theories, on paper. He knew from the beginning what the x's and t stood for. The m's, though, were originally just marks on paper. There was, naturally, an "idea" of mass, but not an operational definition. What I call for the moment an "idea" is closely related to significance as well as to what others, mistakenly as we saw (p. 63), call "conceptual properties." The idea of mass, for instance, is the anticipation of a quantified property of physical objects that does not change in time whatever happens to the object as long as it remains "the same object." The idea of a concept is not yet the concept itself; it is like a promissory note; the actual definition fulfills the promise. One virtue of theory is that it often helps to make good the promise (p. 36). The reason is (and this is one of the most remarkable features of a worthwhile theory) that one can check it against known facts and laws, or at least *begin* to check it, while it still contains "marks on paper," such as, in our case, the m's.

(I hardly need to say that I do not pretend to reconstruct in the next paragraph what went on in Newton's mind. Nor do I follow either his own exposition or the historical order of hypothesis and observation.)

Newton first checked his theory (I ignore the moon) against the known laws of planetary motion, the three laws of Kepler. Since he could deduce them from his theory, he obtained a definition for the masses of the members of the planetary system: the values one must attribute to their "parameters" m in the theory if it is to yield Kepler's laws. (But for a multiplicative constant these values are uniquely determined.) Next he extended the theory successfully to ordinary physical objects or, as one says, terrestrial bodies (the story of the apple!) by deriving from it Galileo's laws of freely falling bodies. This was a tremendous increase in scope and therefore very impressive. Yet the extension does not by itself yield an operational definition for the mass of a terrestrial object. How-

ever, it suggests (notice that I say suggests, not implies) both a law and a definition. The law is

(L) $$\frac{w_{AP}}{a_P} = \text{constant};$$

the definition is

(D) $$\mu_A = \frac{w_{AP}}{a_P},$$

where w_{AP} stands for the weight of an object A at a place P, aP for the acceleration of the free fall at P. Clearly, since (L) says that the quotient that occurs in
both equations does not change with P, μ_A becomes a strong candidate for a mass
concept—provided that the "hypothesis" (L) can be confirmed. (L) was confirmed, though I believe only quite some time after Newton's death. The suggestion that comes from the theory has thus two aspects: one is a hypothesis
(hunch, guess) concerning a law of which nobody would have thought without
the theory; the other a definition that has the desired significance provided the
hypothesis is confirmed. Fully aware as we are of the connection between laws
and significance, we are not surprised at this double aspect of one of the benefits
of theory.

Even if (L) is confirmed, μ_A can have the desired significance only under the
assumption that *"a" physical object that does not change "its" place changes
"its" weight only if we have a good reason to say that "it" is no longer "the same
object."* Consider the following case. A physical object has changed its weight
without changing its place and without there being a good commonsensical reason for its no longer being "the same object." Science discovers that a small
part of it has evaporated. Science and, following it, common sense accept this
as a good reason. But what is in general a good reason? Partly because of this
vagueness I called the italicized statement an "assumption" rather than a "law."
Yet we are presumably dealing with the significance of weight and I have so far
explicated 'significance' in terms of 'law' and not of 'assumption'. Besides,
'assumption' is itself a very vague word. Its vagueness invites further analysis.
Such analysis reveals the complexity of the "idea" of physical identity ("the same
object"). I cannot go into those matters here, not even in small print, even
though they are very interesting. Until recently they were also very important in
the philosophy of physics. They lost some of their importance when it turned
out that the "particles" of the partially interpreted calculi that are now employed
do not "move" in orbits. For there is not much point to a notion of physical
identity which does not imply that a "physical object" (or a "particle," which is
supposed to behave (on paper) more or less like a physical object), if "it" is to
remain "itself" when changing "its" place, can only move in orbits.

PROCESS

In the last section I broke a rule I made for myself. So far, whenever I
used for the first time a word or phrase I intend as a technical term, I

always italicized it and then proceeded directly to explicate it. In explaining the paradigm I used 'system' and 'state', both of which I intend to use technically, without introducing them in this manner. The reason is that *system* and *state* are two of five terms that are best explicated together. The other three are *process, closure,* and *complete set of relevant variables.* Nor shall I now explicate them directly. It will be advantageous to use them for a while more or less naively in the consideration of some aspects of our paradigm and to attempt a more formal explication only afterwards. By then the reason for this procedure will be apparent.

If one disregards features of our paradigm one can arrive at schemata of laws or theories that are in some respect of the same "form." (This use of 'form' is by its very nature ambiguous; but it is also quite unproblematic and rather convenient; so I shall not tarry to explain it.) The schema I am about to outline is that of a process law or process theory. I say law or theory, because a process law is so high an achievement that we are not likely to know one without knowing a theory from which it follows. Or, to say virtually the same thing differently, a process law is so complex a statement that more often than not it will by itself amount to a theory. Surely this is so in the case of our paradigm. But for my present purpose the distinction between law and theory does not matter. (This is why I decided a while ago to postpone the examination of those features of our paradigm that make it a theory.)

A state is a state of a system; certain classes of states, one for each value of the time variable, are processes; a process is thus the temporal unfolding of a system. This indicates how the several ideas depend on each other. For the moment it will suffice to think of a system as a group of physical objects in a limited piece of space that remains identifiable as a group through an appreciable length of time. I say identifiable as a group because some of the objects may during the time interval disappear (example: chemical reaction in a sealed test tube). What is an appreciable length of time depends on the universe of discourse (example: an interval so considered in quantum mechanics may not be one in social psychology). In our schema the identity or identifiability of the system appears as the time-independence of its description; in our instance, of the numbers m. The constant masses of the moving bodies are a specially simple and intuitive case; naturally, since this is one of the virtues a paradigm ought to have. The schema of quantum mechanics is at the other extreme. (That quantum mechanics is a partially interpreted calculus is quite irrelevant for these "formal" considerations.) There it takes some effort to see clearly what the "self-identical" system is; and the result is anything but intuitive. In the Newtonian case, the "system bracket," if I may so express myself, is a finite set of single numbers, each the value of a relatively simple, though implicitly relational property of one of the constituent objects; in the (infinite) system bracket of quantum mechanics the place of each m is taken by a specified function of several variables. The one essential feature, that is, the one I select in order to arrive at a "form," is the time-independence of the system bracket. But one must not forget that even in our simple case —and that goes for the "state brackets" as well—even single numbers are again like the nonsubmerged parts of icebergs. Such a single number may be the numerical value of a quantified relational character. Position and velocity coordinates are indeed of this kind. A state description, too, is the joint assertion of several statements of individual fact. It says that some properties and relations are exemplified in a system at a certain moment. I shall schematically write $C = [c_1, c_2, \ldots, c_m]$ for (the description of) the system, $S^t = [x_1{}^t, x_2{}^t, \ldots, x_n{}^t]$ for (the description of) its state at time t.

To specify a process one must specify (1) what the system is, (2) what a state of it is, and (3) the law, or, as I shall also say, the process law. This yields the following schema. Given the system, $[c_1, c_2, \ldots, c_m]$, and its state at a certain moment, $[x_1{}^{t_1}, x_2{}^{t_1}, \ldots, x_n{}^{t_1}]$, the law permits the computation of all other states (the state at any time t) of the system. In other words, to know the law means, in principle, to know n functions of $m + n + 1$ arguments, namely

$$x_1{}^{t_2} = f_1\,(c_1,\; c_2,\; \ldots,\; c_m;\; x_1{}^{t_1},\; x_2{}^{t_1},\; \ldots,\; x_n{}^{t_1};\; t_2 - t_1)$$
$$\text{(P) } x_2{}^{t_2} = f_2\,(c_1,\; c_2,\; \ldots,\; c_m;\; x_1{}^{t_1},\; x_2{}^{t_1},\; \ldots,\; x_n{}^{t_1};\; t_2 - t_1)$$
$$x_n{}^{t_2} = f_n\,(c_1,\; c_2,\; \ldots,\; c_m;\; x_1{}^{t_1},\; x_2{}^{t_1},\; \ldots,\; x_n{}^{t_1};\; t_2 - t_1).$$

I say in principle because even when we know processes, as we do in physics, the law is not actually stated in this form but, as I mentioned before, as a system of differential equations which one must solve in order to arrive at a pattern exactly like (P). In the case of mechanics the development of the arithmetical tools necessary to achieve the solution in the general case took about two hundred years!

I suggested that we think for the time being of a system as a group of physical objects in a limited piece of space identifiable as such during an appreciable length of time. I turn now to the explication of the clause "in a limited piece of space." The idea involved is that of (spatial) closure. I shall begin with an imaginary story. Evidence accumulates, at first barely above the limits of measurement but eventually more and more pronounced, that the planets no longer move as they should according to our theory. There are two possibilities. Either we can or we can't trace the discrepancy to some supervening circumstance. If we can't, then we shall eventually give up the theory. Or we find the supervening circumstance. One of the simplest things that might occur in this case—I mean logically simple—is that we discover a dark fixed star coming so close to our solar system that its gravitational pull can no longer be neglected in computing the orbits of the planets. What I call logically simple may well spell the end of our world. Probably the prospect would upset quite a few. As far as the theory is concerned, though, nothing has happened; at least, nothing that would either surprise or upset us. Naturally, Kepler's laws will not hold if there is another body close enough to exert an appreciable pull. The situation is reflected in the nature of the "new" variables, those one must now introduce because of the "supervening" circumstance. They are merely new instances of the old kinds, that is, of those variables that do occur in our theory. What we need to know in this particular case is the mass of the new star, its distance from the sun, and its velocity at a certain moment. (It is safe to say that as long as we shall be alive the whole solar system can be treated as a point.)

Now for the lesson to be learned from this story. We saw before that whenever we state a law we assert, by omission as I put it (p. 75), that no circumstance it fails to mention is relevant to its truth. This includes unmentioned instances of the kinds of variables the law does mention. My first point is that while we do not always pay much attention to this feature, we take it seriously when we try to achieve a process formula. Secondly, it is quite impossible for us to describe anything but a limited piece of space. That it may be huge (provided the description is very selective) is shown by astronomy; but again this does not affect the principle, except for some subtle and difficult speculations, which we can safely neglect, about the "finiteness" of the universe. Whenever we state a process law we assume, then, that the system is closed: what happens inside our piece of space to the relevant variables (i.e., the variables the law mentions) is not affected in any way by any factor outside of it, whether this factor be an additional instance of one of the kinds of variables that occur in the law or something else.

The notion of closure would not be as important as it is if we did not in many cases know how to bring about closure. Probably the best illustration comes from thermodynamics. Consider a system consisting at a certain moment of a certain quantity of ice, a certain quantity of water, and a certain quantity of air of a certain humidity, all of known temperatures and enclosed in a certain volume. From this information thermodynamic theory can predict the course of the process, i.e., future temperatures, humidities, quantities of ice, and so on—provided the system is closed. In this case, closure means thermic insulation. To expect any theory to predict what will happen in the container irrespective of whether or not it is either insulated or heated or cooled from the outside would be foolish indeed; at the least, it would be unusually naive. Thus, as our piece of space is in this case represented by the container, so the closure of the system inside it is secured by making it of thermically insulating material. The example also lends itself to a refinement of the notion of closure. Quite plausibly, the theory can predict the course of events (S^{t_2} from C and S^{t_1}) inside the container even if the latter is not insulating provided only that it is known for each moment of the time interval over which the prediction extends (from t_1 to t_2) how much heat "flows" through the walls of the container in either direction. The perfect arithmetical schema of this situation are the so-called boundary conditions of a partial differential equation. To solve such an equation one must know those conditions. Fortunately, though, one does not need to understand this arithmetical representation of the idea in order to grasp the idea itself. Practically it is very important, since often, when we cannot produce insulation, we can post "border guards" to register what "comes in" and what "goes out." (For instance, we cannot "turn off" gravitation.) Insulation is merely a special case of known boundary conditions. Thus, to say that if a process law is to be applied the system must be closed is not to say that it must be insulated. It suffices to know what "enters" or "leaves" through the boundary of the "limited piece of space" during the time interval over which the prediction extends. This is the sense in which I shall speak of closure.

One more example from an entirely different field. It takes a good deal for granted, much more than I, for one, consider reasonable. This will come out later. But the example, or, rather, the story, has the virtue of bringing home the notion of closure with some force. Assume that in 1850 anthropologists visited an isolated Pacific island long enough to gather information that contains the C and the S_{1850} required to predict future states of the society they found on the island by means of a process law, which they either then knew or later discovered. This law also permits the inference that the interference caused by the expedition itself was negligible. In 1950 the prediction S_{1950} proves patently false. Nobody is surprised. During the last war the island was occupied by American troops. Thus, closure had been broken.

Incidentally, the story throws some light on the relatively recent wordy controversy between the two anthropological "theories" of parallelism and diffusion, which in turn furnishes a good illustration of the loose use of 'theory' I mentioned (p. 34). Parallelism is not a theory but a very crude developmental law to the effect that primitive societies if left to themselves go through certain (rather vaguely defined) successive stages. The diffusion "theory" is not even a crude law; it merely asserts certain individual facts which, as it happens, are rather hard to ascertain, namely, that the societies cited as evidence by the parallelists did in fact interact with others that were, as the parallelists would put it, at different stages of development.

As we ordinarily use 'closure', two different features of a process schema could plausibly be so called. In order to compute (predict) by means of the process law the future (and past) values of the relevant variables one need not know anything about any variable *outside* the limited piece of space. As I shall technically use 'closure', it refers to this feature and to nothing else. But we also notice the following. In order to compute (predict) the future (and past) values of the relevant variables one does not need to know anything about any other variable *inside* the limited piece of space. This is the second feature. I shall call it the completeness of the set of relevant variables. Literally the distinction between closure and completeness is thus that between the inside and the outside of our limited piece of space. Practically it amounts to this. If the "system" is not closed we have most frequently omitted an outside variable which we would have taken into account had it been inside. When the set of variables is not complete we have most frequently overlooked a variable which is in fact relevant and which is of a kind that does not occur in the "law." This shows that some distinction should be drawn. The way I drew it, in spatial terms, is perhaps the easiest way to draw it precisely.

The values of variables are characters, often very abstract ones. An acute reader may therefore be puzzled by my so blithely locating variables in space. I spoke indeed very concisely. Here is the necessary explication. The characters in question are all exemplified by one or, in the relational case, several physical objects. When I say that a variable is inside a piece of space I mean that the object or, in the relational case, all the objects (example: distance) that exemplify its values are inside this piece of space. Analogously, if the distinction is made, for higher-type characters (p. 43).

As we ordinarily use 'process', we often mean no more than a temporal sequence of events. This idea requires no term of its own, except perhaps for the sake of idiomatic convenience. When we use 'process' more specifically, as we sometimes also do, then it refers to the temporal sequence of the "states" of a "system" *as predicted by a process law,* either one that we know and could actually apply if we went to the trouble, or one we expect to discover, or one that could at least in principle be discovered and applied. This is the technical sense in which I shall use 'process'. From our paradigm and the thermodynamic example we know that there are temporal sequences of events believed to be in fact processes for reasons as excellent as one can ever hope to have within the inescapable limits of measurement and inductive "uncertainty." Of course, this is a matter of fact, not of logical or any other "necessity." (I cautioned against the fuzziness of 'necessity' some time ago.) Yet this very fact can become a source of puzzlement in the light of what was just said about closure and completeness; for these two requirements, closure and completeness, seem so stringent that one may well wonder how anything less than "everything" could ever go through a process. More precisely, one may wonder how a system not extending through "the whole of space" could ever be closed and how any set of variables containing less than "all" variables could ever be complete. Two points need to be made. For one thing, there actually are, at least within the limits of measurement, processes comprehending considerably less that "everything." And there is an obvious sense in which it makes no sense to puzzle or argue about facts. For another, one may indeed wonder whether it even makes sense to say that there is one and only one process, namely, that of the "world as a whole." Practically, if this were so, we would never know it. About that there is no argument. If, on the other hand, we were by some miracle furnished with the C, the (P), and an S^{t_1} for this universal process, it would, I think, make sense to say that as far as we know the world goes through it (and is therefore comprehensively lawful) provided that all the observations we can actually make at times later than t_1 fit into this monster schema. We shall have two occasions to recall these ideas, though each time but briefly.

Suppose there is a group of physical objects, of the sort I called a "system," for which a scientist tries to find a process law. With the descriptions he uses, $C = [c_1, c_2, \ldots \ldots, c_m]$ for the system, $S^0 = [x_1^0, x_2^0, \ldots \ldots, x_n^0]$ for its initial state, the attempt fails. Our scientist changes the two "brackets," replacing C by C', S^0 by $S^{0\prime}$. Each or at least one of the two new brackets contains in addition to all or some of the old items several or at least one new one; for instance, $C' = [c_1, c_2, \ldots \ldots, c_m, c_{m+1}]$, $S^{0\prime} = [x_1^0, x_2^0, \ldots \ldots, x_n^0, x_{n+1}^0, x_{n+2}^0]$. With these brackets our scientist is successful. We are tempted to say that the "physical system" and the "physical state" are the same as before. We merely found it necessary to describe them both more accurately for the purpose of establishing a process law. Fancifully one might add that reality is inexhaustible by any description. With some of the sense and nonsense behind this fancy we shall deal only much later. Between the two, the sense and the nonsense, there is as usual a twilight region. To see clearly in this twilight, assume that we are looking at two "physical systems," saying, as we often do, that they are identical or the same. Since there are two "physical systems" and not one, we are not speaking of logical sameness or identity. Upon a little reflection we see that we mean two things. (1) The two brackets C and $\bar{C}$ by which we describe the two groups of objects are of the same kind. I shall show what this means by an example. If C consists of ten numbers, each the value of the mass of a physical object, then $\bar{C}$, too, consists of ten numbers, each the value of the mass of a physical object. The general statement is as tedious as it is obvious. (2) Corresponding values of the two brackets are literally, that is, in the logical sense of identity, the same: $c_1 = \bar{c}_1$, $c_2 = \bar{c}_2$, $\ldots \ldots$, $c_m = \bar{c}_m$. What goes for "system" goes for "state." To obtain for states the two statements corresponding to (1) and (2), one merely has to replace C and $\bar{C}$ by S^t and

$\overline{S}^t$ respectively in (1), and the c and $\overline{c}$ by the x^t and $\overline{x}^t$ respectively in (2).

When we say that two "physical systems" are the "same," which of the brackets are we talking about? Or, as perhaps some might prefer to put it, which brackets ought we to be talking about? The difference between the two questions makes no difference. The one thing we can mean if we are to mean anything reasonably specific is that there actually is, or that we hope to find, or that there is in principle a successful process schema and that for the two "physical systems" the brackets of this schema have the properties I just listed under (1) and (2). This explains why at the beginning of the section I insisted that if one wants to proceed formally in explicating the five notions of system, state, process, closure, and completeness (of a set of relevant variables), one must explicate them all together. Now that we have done this, we see that no further explication is necessary. And I have also (in a crucial instance) demonstrated a more general point I made earlier. I have shown, not only that the five notions in question are best explicated by means of a schema, but that *in any precise and final sense they are nothing but features of a schema.* If we forget this when we apply them to things ("physical systems") or, as some lovers of big words might say, when we apply them to reality, we run the risk of double confusion. We would be confused if we thought that process schemata "must" apply to everything or, for that matter, to anything; and we would be equally confused if we thought that the "perfection" of the process schemata which we have reason to believe apply exempts them from the inescapable limitations of measurement and induction. This is why I spoke so laboriously of groups of objects instead of systems and, when I used 'physical system', surrounded the phrase by double quotes. Now I shall drop these tedious precautions.

This concludes what one might call a minimum explication of 'process'; but it is not all I intend to say about the notion. Taking up a thread of thought I left pending, I shall *first* of all explain why I called process knowledge (i.e., the knowledge of a successful process schema) perfect knowledge. *Second,* I shall take another look at the notion of a complete set of relevant variables, not because my earlier remarks cannot stand alone but, rather, because it pays to distinguish this notion from another. Doing this we shall encounter cross-sectional laws. *Third,* I shall discuss the so-called mechanistic and deterministic aspects of process. Since every system is also a "system of interaction," I shall explicate, *fourth,* the notion of interaction. *Fifth* and finally, since the word 'field' has recently spooked through psychology, I shall say something about the distinctive features of the systems called fields.

As far as it goes and as far as its *relevant variables themselves* are concerned, a process theory (or law) is perfect knowledge. To dispose of the first of the two qualifying clauses, "as far as it goes," consider two process theories such that the second is a deductive consequence of the first without the first being a deductive consequence of the second. Clearly, the first possesses one kind of excellence, namely, scope, to a higher degree than the second. The first qualifying clause indicates that this is not the kind of excellence I have in mind when I call process knowledge perfect. Before explaining what I do have in mind, let me undo a distinction that has served its purpose, namely, that between the c's and the x's. The reason why it must be made in certain contexts is clear enough, I trust. The c's are the (temporally) constant identifiers of the system, the (temporally) variable x's the characterizers of its states. But the c's themselves vary from system to system and their being different makes a difference—naturally, since they occur in (P)—for the processes in the respective systems. (Consider, for instance, two Newtonian systems consisting of the same number of bodies, of different masses but, at a certain moment, of the same positions and velocities. The orbits will not be the same.) Thus the c's, too, are, in an obvious sense, "variables," which makes it convenient to speak in some contexts, when there is no danger of confusion, of both the c's and the x's of a system as its variables.

Formally, this situation is expressed by the circumstance that one could and, in a sense, should add to the n equations of (P) the m further ones:

$$\frac{dc_1}{dt} = 0, \quad \frac{dc_2}{dt} = 0, \ldots \ldots, \frac{dc_m}{dt} = 0.$$

Informally, scientists mark it by writing others than the last letters of the alphabet $(x, y, z, \ldots)$ for the c's and, when speaking about them, by calling them "parameters." The fundamental importance which the distinction nevertheless has, leading me to proceed as I did, is due to the fact that if there is to be a system at all, there must be some time-independent identifiers, though they need not, as in the simplest case, be a set of numerical constants.

Their parameters are, by the way, one of the more obvious sources of the power of process formulae. Take the Newtonian case of two bodies. Depending upon the values of their masses and their positions and velocities at a certain moment, all sorts of processes may occur. The two bodies may fall into each other; they may become double stars; the smaller may become a planet of the larger; or its orbit may merely be bent toward that of the larger, in which case we call it a comet. What happens, broadly in terms of such categories as well as in every detail, depends on the initial state as well as on the two masses. To expect, at this stage of the discussion, a separate specification of these dependencies would be silly; the source of all such specifications is, of course, (P) itself. On the other hand, it is also worth noticing that there was, before Newton, no good reason whatsoever to consider the orbits of planets and of comets as "special cases" of the "same" law. (The circumstance that they are all conic sections is at best a hint.) Similarly, there was at the time of Aristotle no good reason to consider the celestial bodies as "bodies" in the same sense in which ordinary physical objects (or, as they then said, sublunary ones) were "bodies." In this sense Aristotle's *quinta essentia* was really the most economic assumption and Anaxagoras was a rather wild-eyed theorist. Yet he was right or, perhaps better, his was the visionary insight.

Consider now a variable of which we have process knowledge. In other words, we know or we know how to find the (smallest) closed system among whose relevant variables it occurs. ('Closed' in 'closed system' is really redundant; but sometimes redundancy helps.) Thus we know all the other variables with which our variable "interacts." (I have promised to explicate 'interaction' later. But in this context the word is clear.) We know, in particular, how to compute the future as well as the past values of our variables from what we can now measure (provided we also know the past or future boundary conditions). Retrospectively we know, furthermore, what the present value of our variable would have been if some earlier state of the system had been different from what it actually was. Prospectively, we know how to influence its (and the other relevant variables') future values by present interference with the system from outside; and we also know the limits of such interference. What else, I ask, could we possibly want to know about this variable in a scientific way? But I had better stop to consider what I am doing. I set out to explain the "perfection" of process knowledge and find myself asking a rhetorical question: What else could we possibly want to know in a scientific way? This did not happen by chance. Nor do I try to get by with mere eloquence. What precedes the rhetorical question is already the explication of what I mean by perfect knowledge. It shows, I think, what scientific knowledge is by showing what it is in the ideal limit. The story of the boiling pot was simple enough to give the idea; Newton's story is complex enough to give the ideal. Understanding them both, we understand the nature of science.

The other qualification in the opening sentence of the next to the last paragraph, "as far as the relevant variables themselves are concerned," must still be explained. Once again, two examples will get us to the point more quickly than a general statement. Assume, quite unrealistically, that we actually have a process theory of human behavior whose relevant variables are all either environmental or of the kind now used in clinical psychology. This is the first example. Or, remember that so-called phenomenological thermodynamics, which counts temperature, heat, pressure, and so on, but no atomic notions among its relevant variables, is in fact an excellent process theory. This is the second example. In the first case, we may still want to know what connections, if any, there are between the clinical variables and those of physiology; or, to say the same thing differently, we may want to know how people's behavior is connected with what goes on inside their bodies. In the second case, we may wish to in-quire whether and how, say, the temperature and the heat content of a gas are connected with properties of the particles that presumably make up the gas. This shows why I added the qualification "as far as the relevant vari-ables themselves are concerned." One might wonder, though, in view of the stringency of the closure and completeness requirements, whether there could be any such "connections" at all or, if there are, of what special kinds they would have to be. 'Connected' and 'connection' are vaguer than the words I usually employ. The reason is that I wish to postpone the necessary analysis until the next chapter. But I should like to mention now that the issue touches upon a point I made before, announcing that it would subse-quently be touched upon twice (p. 97). Whoever wonders what "connec-tions" there could be between the variables within and those without a complete set will soon be led to wonder how anything less than everything could possibly go through a process.

It is an amusing logical exercise to explore the following possibility. "All" the variables fall into two classes. No process law contains variables from both classes and there are no other "connections" of any kind between the two classes. There is no logical difficulty whatsoever in this schema of a "dualistic" universe, even if each of its "halves" is comprehensively lawful. What goes for two goes for any number of such mutually exclusive and disconnected sets of variables. In the case of two, we have a model of what could reasonably be meant (in a peculiar sense of 'reasonable') by those who assert a "dualism" of "mind" and "body." However, it is not what they actually mean, if for no other reason than that they admit or even insist on some connections. There the logical difficulties begin. Of this later.

Now for a second look at the notion of a complete set of relevant vari-ables. As we now speak, it consists of both C and S^t; I shall call it V and assume $t = 0$. Choose an arbitrary value for each variable in V. The set is a (complete) set of *independent* (relevant) variables if and only if each such choice corresponds to a possible state of a possible system. If, for this to be the case, the values must fulfill certain conditions, then the vari-ables of V are not independent. The notions of completeness and inde-pendence must not be confused with each other. Take our original example, a system of ten celestial bodies. As we now use 'variable', its V is an ordered set of seventy numbers, $[m_1, m_2, \ldots m_{10}; x_1^0, x_2^0, \ldots x_{60}^0]$. Its variables are not independent. The conditions any set of seventy num-bers must fulfill are these: (1) the ten m's must all be positive; (2) no two position triples must be identical, e.g., if (x_1, x_2, x_3) and (x_4, x_5, x_6) are the position coordinates of two bodies, one must avoid choices such that $x_1^0 = x_4^0, x_2^0 = x_5^0, x_3^0 = x_6^0$ are all true. Or, assuming that the positions are given not by the coordinates of the bodies but by their mutual dis-tances, let d_{12}, d_{23}, d_{13} be the distances of three of the bodies. Each d^0 must then be a positive number and, more interestingly, if the values of two of them, say d_{12}^0 and d_{23}^0 have been chosen, the choice of the third is subject to the condition $d_{12}^0 - d_{23}^0 \leqq d_{13}^0 \leqq d_{12}^0 + d_{23}^0$, which is of course the familiar theorem that a side of a triangle is not smaller than the difference and not greater than the sum of the two others. Again, assume that the positions are given by both angles and distances and that d_{12}, d_{13}, d_{23}, and a_{123}, the angle between d_{12} and d_{23}, are among the variables. d_{13}^0 is then uniquely determined by d_{12}^0, d_{13}^0, and a_{123}^0. The way I defined a complete set of relevant variables contains nothing to exclude even such obvious redundancy. Incidentally, we see that a system may have more than one set of relevant variables. (Arithmetically this is rather obvious.)

The examples I chose are geometrical. This was not by chance. Geometrical laws are the most striking examples of *cross-sectional laws*. ('Cross-sectional' is taken from the metaphor that considers a state a temporal cross-section of a process. A so-called still or frame is in this sense a cross-section of a film.) Such laws state functional connections obtaining among the values which several variables have at the same time. There is a hard core of cross-sectional laws, including those of geometry, that cannot be deduced from or in any other sense be "reduced" to process laws. All-important as they are, process laws are therefore not literally all of science, not even in the ideal limit. The nature of cross-sectional laws is best understood by distinguishing them from so-called equilibrium laws on the one hand and from definitional connections among the variables of V on the other.

Take the law of the lever, $p_1 d_1 = p_2 d_2$, which I used as an illustration once before (p. 32). Since the four letters stand for the values the four variables have at the same time, one might at first sight mistake the law of the lever for a cross-sectional law. In this respect there is indeed no difference between the two kinds of law; yet there is in another. A cross-sectional law states a functional connection that obtains under all circumstances (provided the law is true). An *equilibrium law,* such as the law of the lever, says that some change will occur if the connection its formula states does not obtain. Accordingly, the equilibrium laws of a system follow deductively from its process law, but not necessarily conversely. In this sense equilibrium laws are expendable; some cross-sectional laws, we saw, are not. To grasp this more firmly, consider that we know the (P) of a system. Clearly, it is a purely mathematical job to determine those V's for which a certain x, or certain x's, or certain functions of certain x's remain constant for $t > 0$. (If we choose the x's or the functions beforehand, then there may be no such V's. If, however, (P) is a system of differential equations, then there are always some such functions, technically known as intermediate integrals. This is the root of the so-called conservation principles of physics. If, on the other hand, one knows some equilibrium conditions of a process, one does not by this token alone know the law of the process. For to know that if certain conditions are fulfilled no change will occur (in certain respects) is not the same as to know what will occur if they are not fulfilled. (Technically again, a "complete" set of intermediate integrals is equivalent to (P).) Equilibrium laws are just one kind of imperfect knowledge. Another name for them, taken from mechanics, is static laws or laws of statics. Process laws, on the other hand, are the most accomplished dynamic laws or laws of dynamics, which is but another phrase for "laws of temporal change." This is the only good meaning of the traditional dichotomy statics-dynamics. I thought I had better mention it, since both words, particularly 'dynamics', are used a good deal in the philosophy of the behavior sciences. As we see, it makes sense to say that these sciences should search for dynamic laws. All sciences should. As we shall see in Volume Three, it is one of the outstanding contributions of the Functionalists to have set psychology firmly in this direction. But there are also ideological uses of the two words, 'statics' and 'dynamics'. Of these later.

Having distinguished cross-sectional laws from equilibrium laws, I turn now to the distinction between the former and definitional connections. Assume that a complete set V has a subset V' such that all the variables that are in V but not in V' are defined or definable in terms of those in V'. Obviously V' can be used instead of V. Doing that, one will also get rid of some of the "conditions" the value choices for V must fulfill, thus increasing the "independence" of the complete set V' with which one now operates. Only, one must not forget that these "conditions" can be nothing but deductive consequences of the definitions. The latter are, like all definitions, analytic; so are therefore those "conditions." Thus they are not cross-sectional laws which, being laws, are synthetic. It follows that one does not at all do the same sort of thing if "one uses a cross-sectional law to reduce the original number of relevant variables (V) and thus reduces the degree of dependency among the remaining ones (V')." This statement is in fact hopelessly confused. That is why I quarantined it between double quotes. The point is so fundamental that I shall resort to a very nontechnical story which is also, like so many good examples, contrary to fact.

Assume that the biologists' improved language contains the undefined predicate 'red' but that they have only one occasion to use it, namely, when they speak of the hair color of certain people. Assume, furthermore, that a biologist has discovered the following cross-sectional law L: Everybody who belongs to the bloodgroup BG and nobody else has red hair ('for every x: x is a redhead *if and only if* x is a BG'). The discoverer of this surprising law proposes two changes in the biologists' language. (1) 'Red' is omitted from the basic vocabulary; (2) 'red_1' is introduced by the following definition:

'*x* is a redhead$_1$,' for '*x* is a BG'.

(I do not distinguish between 'red' and 'redhead'.) To understand the consequences of the proposed change, imagine that in all actual or possible statements (of the old language) 'red' is replaced by 'red$_1$'. (a) The (old) statements that do not contain 'red' become without change statements of the new language. (b) *L* becomes the tautology '*x* is a BG if and only if *x* is a BG'. What *L* states cannot be stated in the new language. (c) All other (true) laws of the old language that contain 'red' become (true) laws of the new language. (d) Certain individual facts, e.g., that Smith is a redhead, cannot be stated in the new language. It should have been noticed that in telling the story I shifted from 'relevant variable' to 'undefined descriptive predicate'. This shows how fundamental the matter is. By now it should also be clear. If one is primarily concerned with or impressed by (a) and (c), as one may well be for many scientific purposes, then one may think that one still has, literally, the same theory and express this belief by the confused statement I quarantined. In view of (b) and (d) such a belief is clearly mistaken. The hard core of all this can be expressed even more simply. To say 'for every *x*: *x* is *A* if and only if *x* is *B*' is not the same thing as to say that *A* and *B* are "identical" or, perhaps better, that '*A*' and '*B*' name the same character. Readers who are again becoming impatient may assume that '*A*' and '*B*' stand for any two of the following three characters: being in a certain behaviorally defined state, being in the "corresponding" physiological state, having the "corresponding" mental content. This should convince them that we are now acquiring the background which is needed, not only to answer, but even to ask intelligently some of the fundamental questions about psychology.

Technically, the confusion I just cleared up may lead to the belief that a law (which is always synthetic) of the 'if and only if' form becomes, by virtue of this form alone, a definition (which is always analytic). This is indeed one of the ideas that underlie Dewey's philosophy of logic. But one can reject this absurdity without denying the peculiar excellence of conditions that are both sufficient and necessary. Of this later.

The story about 'red' and 'red$_1$' can be used to separate the wheat from the chaff in some claims that have been made for "realistic" languages. Among the main needs of science is accuracy as well as "intersubjective reliability," not in any "philosophical" sense of this slippery phrase but in the ordinary sense in which one gets better agreement, at least among trained observers, if one asks them to read a dial than if one asks them to make statements about colors they see without permitting them to use either the terms or the laws of science. To understand what this prohibition excludes, consider that the characterization of a certain shade of red by the frequency of the (approximately) monochromatic radiation that *causes* us (under standard conditions) to see this shade is incomparably more accurate as well as intersubjectively reliable than its characterization even by a well-trained group of observers possessing a very ample vocabulary of color words who must not do anything but look carefully and then tell us what they see. For their special purposes scientists are thus actually better off if (I speak metaphorically) they accept our imaginary biologists' proposal and restrict the number of their undefined words, or at least their use on certain occasions, as much as possible. If the scientist is willing to pay the price I specified above under (b) and (d), the basic "realistic" vocabulary with which he can get along is in principle surprisingly small. On the other hand, our story shows that the basic vocabulary of a "realistic" language need not and, for philosophical purposes, cannot be quite so limited. This disposes of the silly slogan that science is about "pointer readings" and nothing but pointer readings.

Since velocities are defined in terms of position and time, one may wonder whether the position coordinates of the bodies and time do not together constitute a complete and independent set of state variables for our paradigm. It is well to understand accurately why this is not so. The point is, simply enough, that "time as such" is not among the characterizers either of the system or of its states; it functions (to speak once more as the scientists do) merely as a "parameter." What this shows could be more pretentiously expressed by saying that "time as such" is not "causally effective." This is, in fact, a very fundamental feature of our world or, at least, so it would seem. Of course, this need not be so (see p. 129). Again, all this is not to say that the rate-of-change variables could not in principle enter into cross-sectional laws, though this does not happen to be the case in our paradigm. For we saw earlier (p. 89) that the proper way to think of these variables within a fully articulated process schema is as momentary.

Every (successfully applied) process schema is *mechanistic* in the following sense of this ambiguous word. As long as the system remains closed, one can if one knows its present predict its future. There are no alternatives and there is nothing any part of the system can "do about it." Its future is, as it were, determined by its present. Sometimes this feature is also called *deterministic*. More frequently 'deterministic' is reserved for the extension of the idea of process to "the whole world." A determinist asserts that the world is "comprehensively lawful." This means either of two things. It may mean, rather elusively as we saw, that there is one and only one gigantic process. This is the second and last reappearance of an idea I mentioned before (p. 97). Or it may mean that for any variable we could, in principle, find a process, which is not necessarily that one all-encompassing process among whose relevant variables it appears. This, then, is the thesis of determinism. The most important thing about such a thesis is to grasp firmly what sort of assertion it is. The way I stated the deterministic thesis leaves no doubt that it is, after a fashion, a statement of fact. I say after a fashion because it is so broad and so desperately general a statement, so sweeping an anticipation based on the past and present successes of science that it is, in a sense, not very interesting and, at least to me, not very exciting. On the other hand, it is only fair to point out that some such determinism is, in fact, the frame of reference of all science, including the behavior sciences. This is just another aspect of the profound impact of the Newtonian idea of process. Now I have hinted before that I don't like 'frame of reference'. The phrase is pompous, I think, and it has been ridden to death. Yet one must admit that it has some virtue of suggestion. It suggests, first, that if one did not believe what one's "frame of reference" asserts or implies, it wouldn't be reasonable to do what one actually does; and it suggests, second, that this "belief" need not be explicitly held or, if it is, that one takes it for granted without necessarily having examined it. A frame of reference is not a philosophical position. Philosophy comes in only when one attempts either to prove or to refute such a thesis or frame of reference on "philosophical" grounds. In the case at hand the two "philosophical" parties are the determinists (mechanists) and the antideterminists (antimechanists, voluntarists, indeterminists). As one would expect, both parties use 'mechanistic', 'deterministic', and their cognates "philosophically." The view logical analysts take of their controversy is very dim. Analysis reveals that the issue is wholly and without residue a verbal tangle or, to speak for once with the vulgar, that there is no conflict whatsoever between "science" and "human freedom." Yet it is a matter of record that the impact of this particular controversy has been tremendous, not only in the intellectual history of our civilization in general but also in that of the behavior sciences. Nor is this a matter of the remote past. As late as the turn of the century William James' obsession with a wholly unanalyzed notion of freedom kept him from really understanding what psychology is all about. A glance into the even later writings of Wertheimer, particularly the more philosophical ones, convinces one that the defense of "freedom" against "mechanistic associationism" was one of his dominant intellectual motives. What goes for James and Wertheimer goes equally for Koehler as well as for Dewey, who was one of the founding fathers of Functionalism. The argument still continues, though usually more covertly, among psychologists interested in the philosophy of their field. I can therefore not ignore it completely, though I shall say as little about it as I responsibly can.

The cause of all this hubbub is not hard to find. Assume that a man or a group of men and (a part of) their environment can from without actually be considered as a closed system. As the antideterminists "philosophically" use their words, it would follow that these people are not really "free" to make choices, that it is futile for them to try to live up to their moral standards, and so on, and so on, up or down the ladder of mostly specious arguments from wholly specious premises to those dreaded cynical conclusions which, for better or for worse, are also a part of our tradition. One compromise that has been proposed and that is still being proposed, either overtly or covertly, is that while there is in principle no process knowledge of human behavior, there can be imperfect knowledge about it of the kind that is called statistical. This "compromise" draws some specious support from two sources; first, from the circumstance that a rather large part of our present knowledge in the behavior sciences is in fact statistical; second, from some "philosophical" misinterpretations of the statistical features of modern physics. "Mechanism," or so we are told, has broken down even in physics. I shall say what needs to be said in the next section, both in the main text and, as far as physics is concerned, in small print.

'Mechanistic' occurs not only in these discussions but also on other occasions in the philosophy of psychology. Many of its uses are blurred; some are outright ideological. To trace them, as we must, a brief glossary of the several relatively clear meanings of the term will be helpful. This is as good a place as any to insert it. (a) 'Mechanistic' is used to refer to the broad "frame of reference" or "thesis" I stated above. (b) 'Mechanism' and 'mechanistic' are used as names for the position and the characteristic arguments of those who try, mistakenly as we saw, to anchor the deterministic frame of reference "philosophically." (c) 'Mechanism' is used as the name of a more specific thesis or frame of reference according to which biology is "reducible" to physics and chemistry. Its denial is known as vitalism. The present frame of reference in biology is mechanistic. But the notion of reduction requires analysis. I shall examine it in the next chapter, using the mechanism-vitalism controversy in biology as an illustration. (d) Within physics (more precisely, in view of the theoretical unification that was recently achieved, within physics-chemistry) a theory is called mechanistic if and only if its basic entities are "particles" that "move" in orbits. If "all of physics" is thought to be in the scope of such a theory, then physics itself is spoken of as mechanistic. Contemporary physics is not mechanistic in this sense.

Even a mechanistic physics need not claim that it can literally predict all events in all detail, say, the outcome of a single throw of a die under so-called chance conditions. The point is that the supposedly comprehensive theories of physics have long been partially interpreted calculi. A mechanist (sense (d)) can accept the limits of the interpretation of such calculi as limitations of "deterministic" prediction. Modern physics is not even deterministic in this (reasonably limited) sense. On the other hand, its supposedly comprehensive calculus, quantum mechanics, is a process schema! The basic entities of this calculus, though, are not particles. As to how statistics enters, see p. 124.

Call the several theses by the letters in the enumeration above. It should be noted that the denial of (d) does not entail the denial of either (a) or (c). Nor does the denial of (c) entail the denial of either (a) or (d). As one might expect, this absence of deductive connection is often slurred over in the ideological uses of 'mechanistic'. Some of these latter uses are virtually synonymous with some such uses of 'atomistic' and of 'elementaristic'. Among the ideological contradictories of the latter two one finds 'holistic' and also 'dynamic', which makes 'mechanistic' and 'dynamic' into contradictories. In view of what was said about 'dynamic' and 'dynamics' (p. 103) this is particularly amusing.

'Mechanism' and, synonymously (!), 'dynamism' are also used with some further meanings that are reasonably specific and, I think, quite unproblematic. Biologists, knowing "empirically," as one says, that a certain drug has a certain effect, may search for the chemical "mechanism" that produces it. Similarly, psychologists may (or may not) be interested in the physiological "mechanisms" that "mediate" the lawful connections between behaviorally defined variables. Again, when, say, projection is called one of the "mechanisms" of paranoia, the reference is to two items of (very imperfect) knowledge. 1. Under certain conditions about which we know as yet much less than we want to know, people attribute to others mental contents of a kind they have repressed in themselves. 2. We find that all people showing the syndrome called paranoia, or a very high percentage of them, who attribute certain mental contents, say, hostile attitudes, to others, have repressed such attitudes in themselves.

Now, briefly, for *interaction*. Suppose somebody is told what the variables (C and S) of a (successfully applied) process schema are, but is not told what its (P) is. Then he is told of two systems that differ in one and only one variable. This leaves two possibilities. Either the two systems are identical and their states at a certain time, say, S^0 and $S^{0\prime}$ differ in one and only one variable, e.g., $x_1^0 \neq x_1^{0\prime}$. Or the two systems differ in one and only one index, say, $c_1 \neq c_1'$. For what I have to say there is no difference between these alternatives; so I shall fix the ideas by considering the first. Assume, next, that the person who has been given this information is asked what difference, if any, there will be between two later states of the two systems, say, between S^{t_1} and $S^{t_1\prime}$. Will they be equal? If not, will they differ in x_1 and in x_1 only? Or will they also differ with respect to the values of some other variables, say, x_2 and x_3? Or will they perhaps differ in all variables? The only correct answer is: From what you told me I cannot tell. This is the gist of the matter. But it will pay to elaborate the answer. (Some further elaborations will be found in the next chapter under the heading of additivity.) The reason that our friend cannot tell is that while he has been given C, S^0, and $S^{0\prime}$, he has not been given (P). If he is given (P), he can compute both S^{t_1} and $S^{t_1\prime}$ and then answer all possible questions of the kind we imagine he has been asked. Again, purely verbal elaborations of this statement don't really add anything to it. But since misconceptions in this area played and still play a disastrous role in the philosophy of the behavior sciences, I shall nevertheless venture some comments.

'Depending on' and 'interacting with' are used as virtual synonyms, which does no harm as long as one keeps in mind that the first sometimes also covers the functional connections stated by cross-sectional laws while the second refers more exclusively to the "dependencies" among successive states of a process. What depends on what, then, or what interacts with what and how is a matter of fact. The process formula (P) is the complete source of information concerning all such mutual dependencies or inter-actions among the relevant variables of a process. If one is, like the man in my story, given C, S^0, and $S^{0\prime}$ without being given (P), one must there-fore in principle be prepared to discover that S^{t_1} and $S^{t_1\prime}$ will differ in all respects. On the other hand, there is no reason whatsoever to believe that this will actually be so. The mistaken belief that it must be so I call the dogma of total interaction or, more sonorously, of total dynamic interaction or interdependence. Later on we shall see that this confused idea plays a crucial role in the Gestalt doctrine. After one has discovered a specific process law there is not much point in describing verbally the kinds of de-pendencies that do or do not bind its variables. If, on the other hand, one tries to distinguish and describe such kinds of types by means of the general process schema, one will find that at least some of them correspond to kinds or types of imperfect knowledge. I postpone a closer look at this typology until the next section. An extreme example will be useful right now. Assume that two systems agree in one and only one variable. As it happens, this variable is temperature and the common value is 5000F. Under this initial condition all sorts of systems will tend toward the same state—ashes. Generally, different initial conditions S^0 may lead to the same state of equilibrium provided only that the value or values of a certain variable or variables in S^0 lie within, or above, or below certain limits. Again, this equilibrium may be reached after the same or after different time intervals, depending on the values of the remaining variables; and it may be an equilibrium with respect to all or some of the variables of the process. There is really no end to the variety. The two extreme cases are total dynamic interaction on the one hand and, on the other, the discovery that the system consists of two (or more) closed subsystems. In the latter case there are again two possibilities. Either there is no interaction whatsoever between the two subsystems or there is no interaction provided all or some of the variables have certain initial values. To obtain an illustration of the second alternative, modify our thermodynamic example by using an insulating container with a partition wall and include the thermic conductivity of the wall among the variables of the total system. If the partition wall is com-pletely insulating, then the total system consists of two subsystems.

In view of some recent experimentation and discussion a psychological example should be of some interest. Divide V into two nonoverlapping groups, V_1 and V_2. It may be that as long as the values of the variables in V_1^0 remain within certain limits, the future course of the variables in V_2 is either not at all or (more probably) only to a minor extent affected by variations in V_1^0. If one wants a word to refer to this state of affairs, one may say that the variables in V_2 are *relatively autonomous*. Perception or, more precisely, the perceptual responses of the normal adult members of our civilization determine an area of relative autonomy. How psychologists use 'perceive' and 'perception' I explained earlier (p. 19). What is now involved can be put very plainly. If you and I and Tom, Dick, and Harry are shown a small red cube on top of a large black cylinder, we shall all correctly describe their colors, shapes, and mutual position even though I, unlike the rest of us, am worrying about the next chapter of my book; even though Tom, unlike the rest of us, is hungry and has a splitting headache; and even though Dick's anxieties are, quite irrationally, aroused by the sight of such arrangements. If Harry fails on the colors because he is color blind we are not bothered, for we can systematically account for his failure. The word 'normal', which I inserted above, covers this contingency. Dick's case is more interesting. Probably he will try to "overlook" the arrangement as long as he can. This, however, is a different story. I haven't said that perceptual selectivity and attention are relatively autonomous with respect to personality and motivational variables. This dependency is notoriously rather gross. Even so, if Dick can no longer avoid "looking" at the arrangement, his account may differ from ours. If such be the nature of his neurosis, he may, for instance, see purple where we see red. Studying such cases as his, we shall discover the limits of the relative autonomy of the perceptual response. Some recent experiments have produced some very neat results in this area. But to insist that in view of these results one must no longer speak of perception in isolation from personality and motivation makes no more sense than to reject those thermodynamic process laws which apply only if the amount of heat transformed into mechanical energy is negligible. Interestingly, this unreasonable claim is not made by the designers of the experiments I mentioned but, rather, by some "philosophical" advocates of total dynamic interaction.

One more example. Assume that there is a process schema of the "social process" and that some of its relevant variables are technological and economic. I, for one, would not grant this assumption; but if one grants it, for the sake of the argument, then it would make sense to say, though it wouldn't necessarily be true, that the technological and economic variables determine an area of relative autonomy. As it happens, this is one of the more reasonable interpretations of Marxist doctrine. If it is stated with the proper precautions concerning the questionable part of the assumption, namely, that there is a process law in the group variables, then there is in fact nothing particularly Marxist about it.

Recently psychologists were told that if they wanted to make progress they had better develop a *field* theory. Field theory, so it is said or implied, is the only truly "dynamic" approach; any other is "mechanistic," "elementaristic," or "atomistic," and cannot possibly get anywhere, on purely methodological grounds. The ascendency this verbal fad gained for a while makes it advisable to look into the confusion that spawned it. It stems, quite simply, from failure to distinguish between two meanings of 'field', one specific, one nonspecific. Used nonspecifically, 'field' is synonymous with 'system of interaction' in the sense in which every process schema is a system of interaction among its relevant variables. It follows that all scientists are and at least since Newton always were field theorists. Certainly all contemporary psychologists are. Incidentally, our very paradigm, though it belongs to "mechanics," is a system of total dynamic interaction. So one may well wonder what the advocates of field theory in psychology advocated. Here the second, specific meaning of 'field' comes in. Within physics a certain special kind of process schema is called a field theory; its systems are called fields. At the time the fad appeared in psychology, the prestige within physics of these particular schemata was very high, partly because the general theory of relativity is a field theory in the specific sense. So I shall briefly explain the second, specific meaning of 'field'. This will show that it is absurd to advocate a psychological field theory in the specific sense of the phrase. If one wants to be particularly cautious, one may say that it is absurd at the present stage of psychological knowledge. I don't think that the extra caution is necessary. However that may be, the proponents of psychological field theory behaved as if trying to benefit from the prestige of field theories in physics by usurping an attractive label for their particular ideas. This motive may have been unconscious; probably it was.

Consider an (electrically) insulated hollow sphere made of a thin sheet of metal over which a certain amount of static electricity is allowed to distribute itself. In the equilibrium that is reached almost instantaneously the charges are evenly distributed over the surface of the sphere. Deformation of the surface by means of some mechanism inside it disturbs the equilibrium. After the charges have redistributed themselves, the charge at each point is determined by the shape of the whole surface as well as by the curvature at the point. The principle is that of the lightning rod; with the accurate formula we need not bother. After each distortion equilibrium is reached very quickly, practically instantaneously; thus the speed of the redistribution process in this case may cause one to overlook the difference between equilibrium and process laws. Otherwise this is no doubt a good illustration of dynamic interaction. More precisely, it is as good an illustration as our paradigm. But this is not what some philosophical psychologists thought. Apparently they believed that every "real" or "radical" interaction must be of the kind exemplified by the charged sphere. What, then, is this peculiar "kind"? The answer is that the surface is, in the specific sense of the term, a field.

In our paradigm both system and state brackets are finite sets of numbers.

As I mentioned before, this need not be so. One alternative is for a place in a bracket to be occupied by a function that describes the distribution of a (quantified) character in a continuous piece of space. To understand what that means, imagine that one measures the temperature (T) at "every point" in a certain volume at a certain time. The results can be represented as a function, in the ordinary arithmetical sense of 'function', of, say, the three customary position coordinates, $x, y, z;$ in symbols, $T(x, y, z)$. Of course, one never actually measures anything at "all points" either of a three-dimensional piece of space, or of a surface, or of a curve. Using, as one does, functions of real numbers involves, therefore, the usual idealizations as well as the assumption that theories representing positions in space by the customary real-number triples will not on that score alone run into difficulties. A process schema is called a field schema if and only if at least one of its brackets contains at at least one place a function describing the spread of a character either along a curve, or over a surface, or through a volume. This is the only clear and specific meaning of 'field'. The law of a field schema also has a characteristic form. (P), it will be remembered, does not diagram the group of equations which actually state (part of) the law; rather, it represents the solutions of these equations. Accordingly, the characteristic form of a field law is that of the equations in which the law is actually stated. Let me explain. If one is given a function describing the spread of a character through, say, a volume, then one can, if certain arithmetical conditions are fulfilled, form another function, which describes the distribution over the same volume of a defined character of the sort called a "gradient." A gradient is the rate of change of a character in space, that is, the rate of change in the value of a character as one proceeds, in space, not in time, from a certain point in a certain direction. E.g., if at a certain moment the temperature is the same at all points inside a certain volume, then the temperature gradient is at this moment zero in all directions in all these points. The equations of every fully articulated process schema contain, as we saw, rate-of-change variables, namely, variables that are the rates of change of others in time. Field equations contain, in addition, gradients. Specifically, field equations state functional connections among the gradients and the rates of change in time of the value or values of a character or characters at one point. In arithmetic such equations are known as partial differential equations.

I used a page or so to explain what, strictly speaking, need not be explained in a philosophy of the behavior sciences. Yet the digression was, I think, the most effective way to dispose of the "field" fad. In the non-specific sense of the term, the call for field theories is, as we saw, as trivial as it is unnecessary. In the specific sense of the term, it is, as we now see, absurd.

The real issue behind the alternative field versus nonfield for the axioms of an in principle comprehensive physical theory is that of *action over distance* versus *mediation*. It goes rather deep; so deep that it is closely tied to the very notion of a physical object or, more precisely, to the representation of this notion, or of some features of this notion, in a schema. Two kinds of such representations, call them the *mass point* theory and the *stuff* or medium theory, have long been prominent. At times they competed with each other (Descartes' "plenum" versus Newton's "atomism"); at times they were made to supplement each other (point-electrons in a medium-ether in nineteenth-century physics). Each "formalizes" some intuitive features of the commonsensical idea of a physical object. Both make technically essential use of the real-number model of space and time. The "mass point" is *extensionless,* a mathematical point, as one says, and moves along a strictly one-dimensional line, its orbit. "Stuff" is represented by at least one character (epistemologically, something like Locke's hardness or impenetrability) being spread out *continuously* over a finite volume. The two words I italicized mark the places at which, technically, the real-number feature of the space-time model enters. Let us now see how all this relates to action over distance and mediation.

In a mass-point theory the behavior (I am speaking concisely) of each mass depends on that of the other masses. Since according to the rules of this game two masses cannot be at the same mathematical point, "causes" act in such a theory necessarily "over a distance." Gravitational "attraction" is, historically as well as systematically, the main case. Where there is a stuff or medium, we *imagine* that what happens at one "place" affects first its "neighbors" which in turn affect their neighbors, thus "mediating" the "effect." The intuitive picture is that of a wave spreading over the surface of a quiet pool into which a stone was dropped. I hope it has been noticed that I just spoke of "places," coyly avoiding "mathematical points." There is a gap. *Within a stuff theory* the arithmetical machinery of partial differential equations consistently bridges this gap, just as the form of these equations which I just described represents to the mathematical intuition (whatever that means) the "local" character of the transactions between the characters at a "place" and its "neighbors."

In the last paragraph I have again italicized a crucial word, "imagine," and a crucial phrase, "within a stuff theory." Ever since the triumph of the Newtonian over the Cartesian pattern physics has been deeply committed to an "atomistic" view of matter, that is, to a schema in which the mathematical mass points must somewhere enter. This leads to a difficulty that has never been faced squarely. Its core is that the "image" I mentioned in the last paragraph *must* eventually break down. For if one takes seriously the arithmetical machinery of limits on which the calculus is based and without which one could not even state a field law, then there must be a volume so minute that it contains one and only one particle, quite independently of how attenuated otherwise one's particle notion may be. Action upon particles must therefore eventually be action over distance. I conclude that an atomistic theory of matter is, strictly speaking, incompatible with the exclusion of action over distance. Practically field theories may be very successful for a long time; but they must get into trouble as soon as (if I may so express myself) experimentation penetrates far enough into the realm of the very small.

The idea that field theories can in principle dispense with action over distance bleeds from still another wound. As we now see, its only clear and precise explication is furnished by the form of partial differential equations. The solution of such an equation remains wholly indeterminate as long as we do not know the boundary conditions. And the boundary of a field is clearly not in the immediate "neighborhood" of all its "places." Thus action over distance in some fashion returns through the back door. Einstein, who was of course well aware of this "nonlocal" character of boundary conditions, has therefore recently suggested that physics should, on what he considers to be philosophical grounds, search for a theory which minimizes, in a certain mathematical sense I cannot stop to explain, the import of the boundary. (Technically, his boundary condition is: no singularities.) It must be said, then, that whatever progress such a theory might represent otherwise, as far as action over distance is concerned it would not in the least affect the principle of the thing. All that remains, then, is the idea or, perhaps better, the image of an actual physical medium, which culminated in the ether theories of the nineteenth century. Now I would not be so rash as to assert that such a medium is in the strict sense of producing contradiction incompatible with the special theory of relativity. But it is very safe to say that it would be very difficult to have them both in the same fundamental schema. The special theory of relativity was indeed the end of the classical ether. So it is rather ironical that Einstein was in his later life committed to a physics without action over distance (and, therefore, necessarily with a "medium"). But then, he was also committed to quite "unattenuated" particles that move in orbits and rejected therefore, again on what he considered to be philosophical grounds, the modern quantum theory.

Recently experimentation has penetrated far enough into the realm of the very small to produce the theoretical difficulties I mentioned above. One possible alternative is to return to an unalloyed medium theory. This seems extremely unlikely. Another possibility is, to speak fancifully, the quantization of space and time or, less fancifully, the abandonment of the real-number model for both space and time. In "pure" geometry it is easy enough to construct calculi that may with some intuitive propriety be spoken of as "spaces" whose "elements" (points) are "extended"; and the essentially algebraic and combinatorial character of the Heisenberg form of quantum mechanics may reasonably be taken to foreshadow the eventual superiority of such a space-time representation. To find the right one, if there be a right one, will be a major feat of scientific genius. The philosophical analyst only deals in possibilities. Within science this is, I am the first to admit, mere fancy talk. At best, it will enable the philosopher to say "I told you so" after the scientific genius has done his work. Usually, alas, the line of action is not in this direction. For the most part science puts the philosopher's schemata out of commission and provides him with ideas for new ones. Perhaps our minds are too feeble for this to be otherwise.

If the distinction between fields and nonfields is to be based wholly on the difference between ordinary and partial differential equations, then it becomes even more tenuous. For, as I said before, one can always play mathematical games. As it happens, Newton's nonfield equations are solved by means of an auxiliary partial differential equation that describes how a highly defined mechanical character, the so-called potential, is spread through space. At this point some might say that this does not really make Newtonian mechanics a field theory since the potential is not really a medium. The objection is interesting in that it brings out what is probably part of the complete explication of 'medium': at least one of the characters that are "spread out" must be (in the theory) undefined. For the rest, this objection brings us back to where I was some time ago, namely, to the difficulties of the notion of a medium taken seriously.

In the last section of this chapter we shall encounter so-called historical laws. Coiners or lovers of phrases may be tempted to say that the "action" such laws describe is action over distance in time. One need not be overly impressed with this "analogy." Perhaps it is purely verbal. Besides, we shall see that there are probably no very comprehensive theories whose axioms are "historical."

IMPERFECT KNOWLEDGE

To know a process law is to know everything there is to be known about its relevant variables, at least as far as these variables themselves are concerned. Any other law containing some or all of these variables (and no others) says less and follows in some sense deductively from the process law. I say in some sense because the deduction requires an additional premiss. Consider a schematic case. Examining the (P) of a certain process we discover the following. Let a, b, T be three constants. If $x_1^0 > a$, then x_3 will at some later moment t_1 which precedes T reach and thereafter maintain the value b; in symbols: $x_3^t = b$ for $t \geqslant t_1$ and $t_1 < T$. This, we find from our examination of the process law, does not depend on the values of any other of the variables in S; the only thing depending upon them, as far as the future value course of x_3 is concerned, is the actual value of t_1 (within the limits 0 and T). Thus we have deduced the following law (L): If in a "system" $[c_1, c_2, \ldots , c_m]$ the character x_1 has at some time a value exceeding a, then the character x_3 will *at some later time but before T units of time have lapsed* reach and thereafter maintain the value b. Clearly one can discover such a law without having discovered the process law first. If, on the other hand, one knows the latter then one can deduce the former. The additional premiss in this case is $x_1^0 > a$. Loosely speaking, it amounts merely to a "specialization" of the process. I put 'system' in (L) between double quotes in order to remind us that the strict use of this word involves the idea of process.

Anyone who fully grasps for the first time the subtlety and perfection of process knowledge may well wonder how any generality less subtle and less perfect could ever be true "without exception." If such a one reflects on the schematic example I just gave he will no longer wonder. Even so, he might reasonably expect any law not a process law to have some features that are, so to speak, the marks of its imperfection. There are indeed such features. Probably every law not a process law has at least one of them. (I say probably because I do not see how one could or, for that matter, why one should make a categorical assertion on this point. There is such a thing as specious precision.) In our case the characteristic feature is stated by the phrase I italicized in the formulation of (L): *at some later time but before T units of time have lapsed*. Whether the interval [0, T] is a minute or a thousand years makes no difference in principle. More often than not we do not even bother to specify T; we just say "at some later time" and rely on the context for some reasonable limitation. The characteristic imperfection is that (L) is not fully determinate with respect to time. There is still another kind of indeterminateness by which one can easily spot imperfect laws. I am not overly fond of 'indeterminate'. I use it merely because I think that if a single word can be made to do at all, it is handier than a phrase. Probably the phrase 'width of range' conveys the idea more adequately. It certainly fits better what I now have in mind. A law states that if something of a certain sort is the case then something of a certain other sort will also be the case (I neglect temporal order). Probing more closely what these sorts are, one often finds that the blur at their edges is much larger than it would need to be. Or, if the two sorts are well defined so that there is no such blur, it turns out that their definitions cover a rather wide range of rather different things.

Indeterminateness does not prevent a law from being, in the light of later process knowledge, "without exceptions." Quite to the contrary. One might say that, not being a process law, its indeterminateness is the price it pays for its truth. Other nonprocess generalities have "exceptions." Strictly speaking, they are false. As one usually speaks, they hold only "under ordinary circumstances." This is another phrase that occurs characteristically in imperfect laws; 'under normal conditions' and 'as a rule' are used synonymously. What these phrases mean is that the "law" holds in many cases, though not in all, and that it therefore probably holds "without exception" under conditions as yet either completely unknown or but vaguely glimpsed. To pursue this line of thought is one possible approach to the notion of statistical laws. The time has indeed come when we must pay some attention to that particular kind of imperfect knowledge. But this requires some preparation and some care; so I shall take up a few other matters first.

How an accurate conception of process leads to a typology of imperfect laws is by now clear. The way I proceeded, we have already collected some such types. Equilibrium laws are one; laws of relative autonomy are another. These two require no further discussion. Nor would there be any point in making the taxonomy as precise or as exhaustive as possible. Some further types are worth considering, though. I shall say a few words about those cross-sectional laws which, unlike some others, can be derived from a process schema. Then I shall take a look at developmental laws. There are, third, statistical laws. These three types I shall in this order discuss in this section. Still another type, so-called historical laws, are so important in the behavior sciences that they must be dealt with at some length. I shall treat them in the next section. First of all I want to call attention to one particular excellence of process laws. I saved this comment because I think that now is the time when it will be most effective.

Let C, S^{t_1}, S^{t_2} signify as before. A moment's reflection shows that the process law permits not only the inference I represented by

(1) $$(C \ \& \ S^{t_1}) \longrightarrow S^{t_2},$$

but also

(2) $$(C \ \& \ S^{t_2}) \longrightarrow S^{t_1}.$$

Taken together, (1) and (2) are equivalent to

$$C \longrightarrow (S^{t_1} \rightleftarrows S^{t_2}).$$

In words: If the system is known then any two of its states can by means of the process law be inferred from each other. Or, as one also says, any state of the system is a *necessary and sufficient* condition of any other. The logical connective stating such conditions is 'if and only if'. Take 'If A then B'. If it is true then A is a sufficient condition of B. Similarly, 'If not-A then not-B' or, what amounts to the same thing, 'If B then A', if true, makes A a necessary condition of B. 'A if and only if B' makes each of the two states of affairs a necessary and sufficient condition of the other. Replace 'A' and 'B' by 'S^{t_1}' and 'S^{t_2}'. In the terminology of cause and effect, each cross section of a process is the effect of any earlier and the cause of any later cross section and we can infer the cause from its effect as well as the effect from its cause. A law of temporal change that is not a process law may state conditions that are both necessary and sufficient. To understand this possibility, consider a schematic case. Assume that the examination of a certain (P) yields the following result: 'If $x_1^0 = a$, then at some later moment t_1, $x_4^{t_1} = b$; and if $x_4^0 = b$, then at some earlier moment $- t_2$, $x_1^{-t_2} = a$. In words: If the system exemplifies at a certain time a certain character, then it exemplifies at some later time a certain other character, *and conversely*. Yet most dynamic laws (i.e., laws involving temporal change) that are not process laws state, in fact, conditions that are merely sufficient (or merely necessary). Take 'If a man is hanged by the neck, he will die', a law that has been known for quite some time. It does not justify the inference that if a man is dead he has been hanged by the neck. Perhaps he was shot or poisoned. Or perhaps he died a natural death. It would seem that when we know a dynamic law of some complexity which comprehends all the alternatives of such "multiple causation," then we are at least within hailing distance of process knowledge.

Remember the laws of geometry. They are cross-sectional; yet they cannot be deduced from a process theory. There are other laws of this kind, for instance, such truisms as 'everything green is extended', of which scientists do not ordinarily think as "laws," even though they are synthetic generalities. Cross-sectional laws that cannot be deduced from process laws are not, as I use the term, items of imperfect knowledge. They are much less impressive than process laws; at least, scientists since the time of Newton have not been overly impressed by them. Yet they are in no way logically subordinate to process laws. Rather, they represent a second, logically coordinate kind of lawfulness. It does not follow that no cross-sectional law can be deduced from a process law. To understand this possibility consider a (P) such that, whatever the initial conditions may be, if after some time one variable, say, x_1 reaches a value within a certain range and then stays within this range $(a_1 \leqslant x_1 \leqslant b_1)$, the same holds for another variable, say, x_2 and another range $(a_2 \leqslant x_2 \leqslant b_2)$. This yields the law (I omit the reference to the system involved) 'If $a_1 \leqslant x_1 \leqslant b_1$ then $a_2 \leqslant x_2 \leqslant b_2$', which no longer contains an explicit reference to time, but where the implicit temporal idea is simultaneity. Thus it is a cross-sectional law. Again, this is merely a schematic paradigm of which there are many variations. If the deducible cross-section law is statistical, then a statistical assumption about the initial condition will be needed as an additional premiss in order to deduce it from (P); of this presently. In other cases one of the additional premisses needed may be a condition all states fulfill because of a nondeducible cross-sectional law; and so on, and so on.

More or less crude cross-sectional laws abound in the behavior sciences, where they are also known as trait correlations; in the simplest case, 'Whoever has personality trait A also has personality trait B'. (About the statistical form these laws mostly take see above and below.) Many insights of nonscientific characterology are logically of this form. The psychiatric notion of a syndrome is merely an elaboration of it. Let A, B, C, D, E be five traits. 'Whoever has at least three of these five traits also has the other two' is an instance of syndromatic lawfulness. Our actual knowledge in the field of personality is as yet not so precise. Nor have we as yet actually derived such "static" trait correlations from an actual "dynamic" process law. But the conjectures of the psychoanalysts about the "origins" of the several personality types (another word for 'syndrome'!) which they believe to have described must no doubt be considered as speculative anticipations of a deduction of this sort from an as yet not extant process theory.

A *developmental law* is a crude sketch or anticipation of a process law. 'If a system of a certain kind has at a certain time the character A then it will under normal conditions at some later times successively have the characters (go through the stages) *B, C, D, E, F'* is the schema of a (six-stages) developmental law. So is 'If a system of a certain kind has at a certain time the character *B* then it had under normal conditions at some earlier time the character *A* and will at some later times successively have characters *C, D, E, F'* (Incidentally, neither of these two schemata, the one anchored at *A* and the one anchored at *B,* is a deductive consequence of the other.). Obviously such laws are imperfect; accordingly they contain several of the phrases I called the marks of imperfection. Another of their characteristics is that though closure is hardly ever explicitly mentioned, it is understood that no prediction can be made if closure is violated. It seems that in developmental laws this meaning is carried by 'under normal conditions'. To see that one merely has to realize that the numerous statements of ontogenic regularity which form such a large part of our biological knowledge are all developmental laws. 'This sapling once was an acorn; it will be a mighty oak' is an instance of an obvious three-stage developmental law anchored at the intermediate stage. We do not find it necessary to mention that the sapling must not be interfered with in certain ways. Yet nobody will think that the law has been refuted if this particular sapling will not grow into a mighty oak because a grazing deer will cripple it tomorrow. So far I have always produced a schema to show how imperfect knowledge can be deduced from process knowledge. In this case I shall not bother. The pattern is obvious by now, I trust.

Whatever psychological knowledge we have about so-called maturation and, in general, about the so-called longitudinal "development" of personality is stated in developmental laws. In the history of the group disciplines we find the so-called laws of stages according to which societies (if left to themselves) pass successively through certain "stages." However vague and, very probably, false such generalizations may be, their form is again that of developmental laws. As every student of the behavior sciences knows, Comte and Spencer proposed laws of this sort.

Some may wonder whether by not adding Marx's name to that of Comte and Spencer I am deferring to the fashion of the day. Far from it. Historically, Marx's influence has undoubtedly helped to spread the idea that group behavior is lawful. So has Hegel's. The reason that I did not mention either is not that their conception of this lawfulness is holistic (which, though most probably false, at least makes sense), but that it is even more seriously distorted by the alleged "uniqueness" of the "process." In Hegel this is clear. Marx, Engels, and their various interpreters are in this respect in a remarkable confusion. But there is never any doubt about their holism.

Now for *statistical laws*. Let *A* and *B* be two characters, however simple or complex, either of single physical objects or of systems. The simpler alternative, *A* and *B* both being characters of single objects, suffices to clarify the main ideas; so I shall limit myself to this case. A statistical law states that if each member of a class of objects has the character A then a certain fraction or percentage p $(0 \leqslant p \leqslant 1)$ has the character B. Thus, if such a class happens to have N members, then the law says that N_1 of its members have the character B, where $N_1 = p.N$. Again, this is merely the (schema of the) simplest case of a kind of lawfulness. In other cases the antecedent of the law may state that a certain percentage of the members of the class exemplify A; A and B may be the same character possessed by an object at different times; and so on, and so on. Again, the simplest case provides us with an adequate paradigm to which I shall, therefore, limit myself.

The distinctive features of a statistical law appear in the way we test it. Assume that we want to test one as simple as our paradigm. We pick a certain number k of classes so that each member of each class exemplifies A. Simplify further by assuming that each of these k classes has the same number N of members. Take $N = 100$ and $p = .4$, which makes each of the k numbers $N_1 = 40$. Taken literally as I stated it, the law says that in each class exactly 40 objects exemplify B. Yet we do not expect even a single of these k numbers to be exactly 40. We consider the law confirmed if (I speak very cavalierly about very technical matters) they "scatter" in a certain fashion around 40. This shows that my original statement of the law stands in need of expansion, or explication, or analysis. The key to the analysis lies in the analysis of the statements we make about the outcome of a series of throws of a die or a coin.

Take a (mechanically unbiased) coin. After a fashion, we all know the law that if we continue to throw such a coin, it will half of the time show heads, *in the long run* and *in a random manner*. I said after a fashion because this law, too, has its peculiarities. They are indicated by the two italicized phrases. For one thing, we need not consider a single run of, say, two hundred heads as a counterinstance. We merely expect (if the law is true) such runs to be very rare or "improbable." That shows that the first phrase I italicized requires analysis. For another, we do exclude the possibility that the throws produce (always or most of the time) "regular" sequences of head (H) and tail (T), say, in a simple case, alternation: *HTHTHT*. . . . . That shows that the second italicized phrase requires analysis. These and some other related analyses make up the so-called logic of probability. The difficulties it encounters are considerable. They are outside the scope of this book. I can merely report that they have been overcome and that, if they are once overcome, the logic of statistics offers no further difficulties (p. 68). Technically, all this is very complex. Quite nontechnically, the upshot is that a statistical law if fully expanded always contains in its antecedent a probability law, that is, a law such as that about coins; for instance, a law to the effect that the frequency of a certain character in successive "samples" from a large population "converges" "randomly" toward a certain number in the sense in which the percentage of heads converges randomly toward .5 if we "continue" to throw a coin.

Having classified statistical laws as a type of imperfect knowledge, I must next show that with an additional premiss a law of this form could be deduced from a process schema. As one would expect, the additional premiss is itself statistical. Take a population of systems which are all instances of the same process schema. To fix the ideas, consider the case that these systems all have the same C. Concerning their respective S^0, assume that they all agree in some variables, say, $x_1, x_2, \ldots, x_k; k < n$. ($k$ may be zero.) For the remaining variables, $x_{k+1}, \ldots \ldots, x_n$, make certain statistical assumptions. Assume, for instance, that for 30, 45, and 25 per cent of the systems respectively $x_{k+1} < 0, 0 \leqslant x_{k+1} \leqslant 1000$, $1000 < x_{k+1}$. From such premisses in conjunction with (P) all sorts of statistical laws obtaining among all or some of the relevant variables either at some later moment or during some time interval, or after a certain time has lapsed, can conceivably be deduced. Which laws, if any, can actually be deduced depends of course on the specific form of (P) as well as on the specific statistical assumption. The principle of the thing requires no further comment.

Consider once more our simple paradigm of statistical lawfulness. As we just saw, it could be an instance of imperfect knowledge in the specific sense in which I call some laws imperfect. But I have not shown, nor could I possibly show, that every statistical law we know or may yet discover is in this manner related to a process law. Yet every statistical law is a piece of imperfect knowledge in a further nonspecific sense of 'imperfect'. It must make sense to say of a single object that it has the character B; otherwise the law itself would not make sense. Our law is therefore imperfect in that it does not tell us what it makes sense to ask and what one may well want to know, namely, whether or not any *single* object that has the character A and on which we fix our attention also has the character B. The law merely tells us that a certain percentage of the objects in the classes to which it applies exemplify B; and even this, we saw, is a gross simplification. This kind of imperfection gives rise to a question. One may wonder whether there are not some areas (I dodge for the time being the explication of 'area') where the best we can *ever* do is to discover statistical generalities. Whoever answers this question affirmatively holds a thesis of about the same logical nature (though of course of different content) as that of determinism. Therefore, like the thesis of determinism, this thesis, call it that of *relative chance,* makes sense although, again as in the case of determinism, it is so very broad and so sweepingly anticipatory that it is perhaps not very exciting. For an obvious reason we must nevertheless pay some attention to it. Such "process" knowledge as we have in the area of behavior is so fragmentary, so inarticulate, and so little trustworthy that one may well doubt whether we have any. On the other hand, we do have a good deal of rather solid statistical knowledge about behavior. Also, we saw that some protagonists of "freedom" rest their case on the thesis of relative chance (p. 107). The thesis could of course be true. In some very limited sense it probably is true. The important thing is again to clarify our ideas by making distinctions.

If a die is cast under so-called chance conditions one cannot predict the outcome of "the next throw," not even if the casting is done by a mechanical device. (For certain refined "statistical experiments" such gadgets have actually been constructed in order to eliminate any "bias" a human caster may possibly introduce.) More important, nobody expects that we shall ever be able to predict the next throw. On the strength of this case alone it would seem that the proponents of relative chance are in as good a position as one could hope to be if one proposes so broad a thesis. Yet the nineteenth-century determinists were able to reconcile the quite uncontroversial facts of the case with their thesis (p. 107). This calls for a distinction. The first thing one must do is to put the idea of relative chance where all such ideas belong, in a schema. For determinism I did this before. Similarly clarified, the idea of relative chance (in an area) becomes the thesis that at least one of the axioms of the fundamental theory (of the area) is statistical. (Notice that I say the fundamental theory, not the comprehensive process theory.) Now in physics our fundamental theories have long been of the kind I call partially interpreted calculi (p. 37). It may well be that this calculus is a process schema and that yet in such cases as that of the die the impossibility of anything but statistical prediction follows deductively from the very rules of interpretation of the calculus. This was in fact how the nineteenth-century determinists answered the objection of "the next throw." I want to make this point very clear; so I shall make it again, in a slightly different fashion. In many cases it is "practically" impossible to go beyond a statistical prediction though "in principle" one could. I don't think I need to explain what this means. Ours is a case of "theoretical" impossibility. In other words, it is a deductive consequence of (1) the calculus, (2) the rules of interpreting it, and (3) certain very simple and quite uncontroversial statements of fact, namely, that one could not make the measurements that would yield the description of a system such that the outcome of "the next throw" can be computed from its process law.

The case of the die is as old as it is familiar. Recent experimentation has produced some more recondite phenomena, flashes on screens built into complicated machines, clicks in Geiger counters, and so on, which in this one respect are in the same boat with the next throw of the die. According to present physical theory it is theoretically impossible to achieve anything but statistical prediction about them. These are, as one would expect, the phenomena whose description corresponds to statements of the theory which attribute a character to a single particle. Some students, among them a few very eminent physicists, believe that this newly discovered fringe of relative chance in the area of physics establishes the thesis of relative chance in the area of behavior. Or, if it is not established, it has at least become very plausible. Thus the Newtonian ideal of a comprehensive process theory of behavior is presumably shattered. This strange claim crops up here and there, including the writings of some philosophical psychologists. So it may be well to examine it carefully.

First another distinction must be made. A theory of behavior is one thing; a physiological theory is another thing. Thus it could be that the prospects of an eventual comprehensive process theory of the one kind are either bright or dim, as the case may be, for reasons that do not at all affect the prospects of the other. What connection there is between their prospects depends on the connections between the two kinds of theory. These I shall discuss in Volume Two. As far as the present issue is concerned, it would seem that what those students wish to say is that modern physics makes a place for relative chance in the area of physiology. Surely this interpretation gives them the benefit of the doubt; for what other connection could there be between "behavior" and "physics"? The most reasonable interpretation of the claim is, therefore, that physiological events and those newly discovered recondite physical events are of the same order of magnitude. One does not need to know much physics or physiology (I know little of the first and less of the second) in order to recognize that this claim is scientifically as unsound as it could possibly be. I, for one, think that it is silly. But even if I am wrong, the argument I am analyzing would still be futile. Patently and often quite explicitly the intellectual motive behind it is concern for "freedom." But we see now that relative chance, if its idea is only clearly stated and firmly grasped, has nothing whatsoever to do with the moral and psychological core of human freedom. Unlike Epicurus's gods, man's freedom, such as it is, does not dwell in the interstices between the atoms.

There is nothing paradoxical in the notion of a process schema whose variables are statistical distributions. This shows again how useful it is to clarify our ideas by means of schemata. As far as the present theory of quanta is concerned, an attempt has been made to interpret it in this manner. The attempt failed. Had it been successful it would have been possible to preserve, after a fashion, the idea of particles that have orbits by considering the process schema of the theory as a "statistics of orbits." A similar attempt had been made earlier in the kinetic gas theory. This attempt, too, failed eventually.

The actual structure of the present theory is more complex. Its distinctive feature and disturbing novelty is that it consists of two partially interpreted calculi, call them *I* and *II,* one piled upon the other, as it were. Less meta-phorically speaking, *II* is partially interpreted into *I, I* is partially interpreted into the physical concepts (pressure, mass, current, etc.) that can be defined in ordinary language.

II, the "last" calculus, i.e., the one remotest from the "data," is so-called quantum mechanics. Its basic entities, the so-called ψ's have no similarity what-soever with mass points. But the law of their temporal change is a differential equation in time. In this sense, which I submit is the only clear sense, the "last" calculus or, to say the same thing more ornately, our idea of the physical uni-verse is as "deterministic" as Newton's. But it is not "mechanistic," as Newton's was, in sense (d) of the four meanings of the term I distinguished (p. 107).

The basic entities of *I* are "particles" in that they have position and speed coordinates. But the laws of their "motion" are irreducibly statistical. (This is just another way of saying what I said before, namely, that the calculus *II* cannot consistently be interpreted as a statistics of orbits, i.e., as a process schema whose variables are distributions of position and speed coordinates of the basic entities of calculus *I.*) Thus the basic entities of *I* have in principle no orbits. This is what I have in mind when I say that they are particles only in an attenuated sense. It is again instructive to reflect on this state of affairs. One can construct schemata that represent only part of what is intuitively in-separable such as, in this instance, the position-speed feature and the orbit feature of ordinary physical objects.

The statistical nature of the laws of *I* is the source of the theoretical impos-sibility of going beyond statistical prediction for the recently discovered phe-nomena I have mentioned several times. If the present theory is true, then these phenomena form an area of relative chance. This is what I had in mind when I said that in a very limited sense the thesis of relative chance is probably true. But then, calculus *II* is nevertheless "deterministic." In this respect the logic of the situation is not different from that of "the next throw" of the die.

HISTORICAL LAWS

A plant physiologist undertakes a quantitative growth study of a certain species. The result he expects is a so-called growth curve. He hopes to dis-cover how the two parameters of this curve, the one that determines the rate of growth of the plant and the one that determines its eventual size, say, specifically, its height, depend on such factors as amounts of humidity, irradiation, certain chemicals in the soil, and so on. These are therefore the factors he systematically varies in his numerous experimental plots. So far the story is rather conventional; I must now give it the twist that makes it the vehicle of a new group of ideas. Imagine that our scientist obtains not one growth curve but, in a perfectly clear-cut fashion, two. Assume further that, to increase his puzzlement, he finds that for each of these two curves the arithmetical form of the dependency of its two parameters on the experimental variables is the same. The only difference is that certain con-stants in this function have different values with the result that, say, one-half of the seedlings grow more slowly and less tall than the others. Our man sets out in search of the overlooked relevant variable (or variables) whose different values for the two groups of plants, call them A and B, might account for the difference. This is still routine, just as is the "deterministic" assumption that there is such a variable. Yet he finds no clues of a routine nature. The only difference he discovers is that the seeds he planted came from two different bags, which he had bought at a store. Thereupon our scientist, lest he miss any chance, somewhat reluctantly considers the possibility that the seeds for group A all came from one of the bags, while those for group B all came from the other. He kept no records from which he could learn whether this is actually the case; fortunately, though, enough seeds of both kinds are left to repeat the experiment. (This time, some seeds of each kind are deliberately saved.) The second experiment confirms the hunch. The next step, again routine, is a careful examination of the seeds that were saved. The seeds from the two bags are found to be alike in many respects. Eventually an elaborate microbiological test uncovers in those that produced the slow-growing and stunted plants the "traces" of a disease from which their ancestors had suffered. Further experimentation confirms that this is the difference that made the difference.

Logically, all this is just another case in which a few steps led a scientist to add to his S^0 a new variable, namely, the trace or scar certain past events have left on some of the seeds but not on the others. Whatever fancy there is lies in the story I made up. So let me now give it another twist. Imagine that at the time the experiments were performed those microbiological tests were as yet unknown. Assume, furthermore, that in the absence of any laboratory clues our persistent scientist engages in a different kind of investigation. He learns from the merchant who sold him the two bags that they came from different parts of the country and eventually, after further inquiry, that a certain disease has long plagued the species in the region from which one of the bags came. For the disease is well known; what is unknown is the microbiological test. From there on we may imagine the experiment to proceed as before. Roughly speaking, it leads to the same law. Yet there is an important difference between the two situations and the two laws. Everything I shall say in this section turns on this difference.

Let me for brevity's sake speak of the earlier and the later law. The later law fits, however roughly, into the process schema. S^0 or, generally, S^t consists of the set of values certain variables have at the time 0 or, generally, at the time t. The additional variable, call it the trace variable, is no exception. What makes the difference is the "present" value of this variable or, less elaborately speaking, the presence or absence of the microscopic scar. But I do for once want to speak elaborately. In the earlier situation the additional information consists of a statement or statements describing an earlier or "past" state or states of the system. Again I am speaking elaborately, but by now I trust my purpose is clear. I want to construct the schema of laws that predict the "future" not from the "present" alone but from the present in conjunction with some information about the "past." Such laws, however perfect or imperfect they may be, are no longer process laws. (Yet I shall in describing them continue to use, somewhat inaccurately, the letters C and S.) Let πS^0 and πS^t stand for some information, either partial or complete, about either a state or states in which the system was either at one or at some or at all moments preceding time 0 or time t respectively. Briefly, the prefix 'π' indicates some information about the "past." Then the schema of the earlier law can be diagrammed as follows:

(H) $$(C \& S^0 \& \pi S^0) \longrightarrow S^t, \qquad t > 0,$$

which contrasts with the familiar diagram of the process schema

$$(C \& S^0) \longrightarrow S^t.$$

Instances of schema (H) I call *historical laws*.

The tale I told makes it in a sense harder for me to make my point. Such self-imposed handicaps have their advantages. The difficulty I deliberately created for myself is that the story seems to confirm the unexamined "assumptions" of a "frame of reference." The earlier law is "merely" a historical law. The later law, the one we can state after the "trace" has been discovered, is "no longer" a historical law. Moreover, after it has been stated, the earlier, historical law becomes, in an obvious sense, expendable. The unexamined assumption to which I wish to draw attention is that there "must" be a trace and that a historical law is therefore "necessarily" an item of imperfect knowledge that will eventually become expendable. Very probably this is so. The point is that it is merely a matter of fact, one of those broad "facts" of which "frames of reference" are made. That we take this particular "fact" for granted is one ingredient of the frame of reference that stems from the Newtonian process schema. It is well worth while to understand this ingredient accurately. A few comments should help. I shall devote one paragraph to each, numbering them consecutively.

1. In many cases we have found the trace. The story I told is in this respect quite realistic. This shows clearly that 'historical', as I use it, is the name of a certain structure or form with respect to time which a law may or may not exemplify. Also, a historical law may become expendable long before we have reached process knowledge in its area. Without further explanation it makes no sense therefore to say that an area (not a law), e.g., psychology or physics, is or is not historical. One thing one could

mean is that *at a particular time* our actual knowledge in the area is, was, or will be either partly or, perhaps, predominantly historical. To another, more recondite meaning I shall attend presently. (I find myself again using 'area' before I have explicated it; but again I think this will do no harm.)

2. Aristotle's observations on memory are probably the earliest articulate attempt to state psychological laws. They are historical. So are the various laws of association the classical British psychologists proposed. So are very many of the laws of contemporary psychology, the laws of learning as well as the more ambitious and therefore more elusive generalizations of the psychoanalysts. Small wonder, then, that in Volumes Two and Three we shall have to make use of the notion of historical lawfulness again and again. This is why we must grasp it firmly and see clearly its place among the possible patterns of lawfulness.

3. Like virtually every ordinary word that is made into a technical term, 'historical' has unwanted associations. At the moment it is for us still an open question whether there are any laws of the "social process" or, as it is sometimes put, whether there are any laws of "history." Certainly, I do not wish to hint or to appear to hint that such laws, if there are any, are necessarily historical. To these questions I shall attend much later, in Volume Two. Still with respect to the word, two things may come to mind if one is guided by its ordinary uses; I do not mean either when I call a law historical. For one thing, every law is arrived at by generalization (induction), either directly, or indirectly by deduction from laws so arrived at; and the instances on which the generalization is based, or at least some of these instances, will as a rule lie in the past. In this obvious and entirely nonspecific sense all laws would be "historical." For another thing, in one of the meanings of 'cause' (p. 117), any earlier state of a system may be said to be the cause of any later one. In this sense every dynamic law would be "historical." When I call a law historical I mean neither of these two things but, to repeat, a certain structure of the law itself with respect to time.

4. A developmental law is not a historical law, nor conversely. To understand the difference it suffices to consider a three-stage developmental law (A, B, C) anchored at the intermediate stage (B). For our purposes it may be schematized by 'If $(B$ now) then $(A$ earlier *and* C later)'. The schema of the "corresponding" historical law is 'If $(B$ now and A earlier) then $(C$ later)' or, what amounts to the same thing, 'If $(B$ now) then $(if A$ earlier *then* C later)'. The difference comes out in the difference between the two logical connectives, 'and' and 'if-then', which I italicized.

5. In the first chapter I introduced the notion of historical concepts (p. 66). Among the examples I gave was 'tempered', as said of steel, and 'hungry$_1$', which means by definition 'having been deprived of food during a certain time interval'. The notion of a historical concept is closely con-

nected with that of a historical law. Though the connection is obvious, I shall be tedious rather than too concise and state it explicitly. To have had a certain character in the past is a historical character of the present. Thus πS^0 can be considered as a conjunction of statements attributing historical characters to objects mentioned in the antecedent of the law. It follows that every historical law contains at least one historical concept. Let us also cast another glance at the hunger example. We encountered two further notions of hunger, one defined in terms of stomach contractions (hungry$_2$), one defined in terms of a disposition to approach and consume food (hungry$_3$). Any law connecting hunger$_1$ with either hunger$_2$ or hunger$_3$ is a historical law.

6. Let me describe accurately what happens when a historical law becomes "expendable." Perhaps the most common historical concept, much used in the biological as well as in the behavior sciences, is age. In the case of trees we can replace 'age' by 'number of rings'. Consider a lawful connection between some property of (a kind of) trees and their age. Call the "two" laws that state this connection L' and L'' respectively; L' being the one mentioning age, L'' the one that mentions instead of age the number of rings. Call L the law that states the connection between a tree's age and the number of its rings. L is historical. L'' follows deductively from the conjunction of L and L', but neither L nor L' follows deductively from L''. It would seem, then, that L is not expendable and that instead of having got rid of historicity in this case we have merely limited its scope. In a sense this is indeed so. But there is also the presumption that (1) L will eventually be superseded by a process law that "grinds out" the number of rings as a function of time (notice that I say time, not age), and (2) we are approaching this ideal if we replace L and L' by L and L''. It is instructive to compare this situation with the case of 'red' and 'red$_1$' (p. 104). If I may so express myself, 'red' is as we saw not expendable in an analytical account of what we know. Nor are statements of individual fact about the past (either inferred or memory). This is not so for historical laws and historical concepts. Whether or not we need them depends on the kind of lawfulness (if any) which we discover.

A historical law may be an item of incomplete knowledge; many have in fact turned out to be just that. Nor is it difficult to show schematically how a historical law may be deduced from a process law. Again, I shall not bother to write down the schema. But again, one could not possibly show that every historical law can thus be "projected" against an eventual "ahistorical" process. There remains another possibility, the one our ahistorical frame of reference excludes. Probably it is no more than a possibility. Yet to be aware of it not only helps to understand one's own frame of reference; such awareness is also the best safeguard against the temptation to hypostatize it. There is a further advantage to this awareness, if one wishes to examine the behavior sciences, an area that is at present in fact largely historical. Notice that I said behavior science is at present historical. I did not say that it is "still" historical. Not that I hesitate to commit myself or, perhaps better, to make a prognosis. The point is that an intelligent forecast requires some further distinctions. To these questions I shall attend in Volume Two. Then it will also appear that, when the analytical job has been done, forecasting loses much of its interest. As often happens, the urge to "commit" one's self on matters of this sort is greatly reduced after analysis has, incidentally, bared its ideological sources.

The possibility we must not overlook is a law or theory which, though historical, is in all other respects perfect in exactly the same sense in which a process law is perfect. In this case one would not inappropriately speak of a *historical process*. It could be that the comprehensive theory of some area actually is a historical process. Or, to go even further, since, as we saw, the thesis of determinism makes sense (though, as I put it, only very broadly and therefore not very excitingly), so would its historical variant. In the notation I use it is not at all difficult to write down the schema, call it (P_h), of a historical process law. One merely needs to double the number of "state variables," replacing each of them, say, x_i^0 by the pair x_i^0, πx_i^0, whose second member represents some information about the past values of x_i^0. I write down only the first line of (P_h):

$$x_1^t = f_1 (c_1, c_2, \ldots, c_m; x_1^0, \pi x_1^0, \ldots, x_n^0, \pi x_n^0; t)$$

Mathematicians have for some time investigated the form a historical process law might reasonably be expected to exemplify. For (P_h), like (P), is not the schema of the equations in which the law itself is stated but, rather, that of their solution. Fully articulated process laws are, as we saw, differential equations. Historical process laws of this kind would be so-called integro-differential equations.

A "historical" world would probably have some peculiar features. Their exploration may safely be left to the mathematical students of integro-differential equations. One comment, though, I shall not suppress. Assume a process that is totally historical, i.e., a historical process such that each πS^t comprehends the complete value course of S^t for all moments earlier than t. A little reflection shows that what I just said must not be taken too literally. By the nature of the schema, any S^t in conjunction with its πS^t would determine the process, no matter how remote in the past t happens to be. Thus there is no single past event and, even, no event in any preselected past interval one would have to know in order to predict the future.

In conclusion a few words about the role of time—still, as always, pre-relativistically. As I mentioned earlier (p. 105), the way time enters into the process schema explicates what could be meant by saying that time as such is not causally efficacious. Nor would it be if the fundamental process were historical, though in this case we would probably speak about action over distance in time. This, too, I mentioned earlier (p. 115). But it would still be the "content" of a cross section or an interval rather than "time as such" that we would consider as causally efficacious.

Imagine that our physicists discover a "trend" in some of the fundamental constants, say, the gravitational constant and the charge of the electron. Assume, for instance, that these constants are found to increase very slowly though, to be sure, at a rate ten or twenty times the error of measurement. Or they may be found to change periodically, with a period of 20,000 years and a mild but equally clear-cut amplitude. It is safe to predict that in this most unlikely event our physicists would very stubbornly try either to derive the changes from their fundamental process law or to modify it so that they could be derived. Only as a last resort would they add to it the three equations, without further trying to deduce these equations, which represent the three constants as functions of time. For if they did this they would not only abandon the process idea; they would also make time as such causally efficacious. The main purpose of this tale is, of course, to explain what it could mean to say that time as such is causally efficacious. Needless to add that if this possibility were actually realized, the departure from our frame of reference would be even more radical than in the case of action over distance in time.

CHAPTER THREE

Configurations and reduction

COMPOSITION LAWS

To know what science is one must, as we saw, know what a process theory is. The notion of process was explained in the last chapter. This one concludes the explication of 'theory'. The Newtonian paradigm lends itself to both purposes. However, the feature that makes it a powerful theory need not be stressed when explaining what a process is. I had this in mind when I said earlier that I would treat the paradigm first as a law and then as a theory. Most of what we need to know about the nature of theory has found its place in the first chapter. We remember, for instance, that a theory, in order to be one, must have scope. But we did not then inquire how scope is achieved. In this section I propose to state accurately the feature of theories that accounts for their scope. This will not only conclude the explication of 'theory'; it will also provide the groundwork for the topics I shall take up in the following sections of this chapter.

The laws of a theory are deduced from its axioms. The larger the number of widely different systems whose laws can be thus deduced, the greater the theory's scope. It seems that in order to allow for such deductions at least one axiom must be a law of a peculiar kind. This is the heart of the matter. I said seems because this is another occasion on which a categorical pronouncement is unwarranted. All one can say and all that needs to be said is that this particular feature, the occurrence of at least one law of a certain kind among the axioms, does secure scope; that all known process theories possess it; and that nobody has as yet clearly stated any other feature that could account for what in all known cases can be traced to this particular one. Our paradigm exemplifies this feature. The only difficulty, if one can call it that, is the simplicity of the paradigm. Because of this simplicity one may overlook the feature or not be sufficiently impressed by it. Not that it is simple or easy to solve the equations of Newtonian point mechanics in the general case. Far from it. The simplicity is of the structural kind. One tends quite naturally to think of Newton's equations as a single law, particularly if one thinks of the arithmetical formula, and thus of the theory as one with a single axiom. Now, whether a statement is one law, or two, or more, is in many ways a moot question. For instance, the joint assertion of two generalities connected by 'and', since it is a single sentence, certainly is in some sense one law rather than two. Nor are all the quibbles one could raise as trivial as this particular one. My point is, therefore, not that one must but, rather, that one can think of Newton's "law" as the joint assertion of two laws or axioms, thus making explicit the characteristic feature of a process theory. Some axioms are the process laws of what I call *elementary systems;* some are laws of the peculiar kind I call *composition laws.* In the case at hand there is only one law of each kind, again showing the simplicity of the paradigm. This will do for a preliminary statement; I turn now to the actual explanations; as usual, I begin with a story, once more a scientific fairy tale.

An instance of a law L is a "direct" demonstration (confirmation) of L. A state of affairs whose description follows by a more elaborate inference either from L alone or from L in conjunction with other laws is an "indirect" demonstration of L (as well as of those other laws). According to Newton ordinary physical objects impart accelerations to each other. Consider the case of two iron spheres and let m_1, m_2, a_1, a_2, d_{12} stand for their masses, (the amounts of) their accelerations, and their mutual distance respectively. Then the law reads

$$(N_2) \qquad a_1 = k \cdot \frac{m_2}{d_{12}^{\,2}}, \quad a_2 = k \cdot \frac{m_1}{d_{12}^{\,2}}.$$

The directions of the two accelerations are those represented in Figure 4.

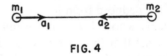

FIG. 4

They lie on the line that connects (the centers of gravity of) the two spheres and point toward each other. (Because of this pattern one also says that two bodies "attract" each other.) Yet everyone knows that the bodies which surround us do not rush toward each other. To demonstrate experimentally the mutual attraction of ordinary bodies as directly as one may demonstrate, say, the law of the lever is indeed impossible. Nor are the reasons for this far to seek. The accelerations are very small, i.e., with the customary units of measurement for mass, distance, and time the factor k is very small; friction is too great; and one cannot eliminate the attractions of other bodies, not to speak of the earth. Some very elaborate late nineteenth-century experiments come reasonably close to a direct demonstration; but even these involve a good deal of inference. What makes my story a fairy tale is the counterfactual assumption that the mutual attraction of ordinary bodies can be demonstrated directly. In the world of this story a scientist could discover the laws of Newtonian point mechanics "directly," more or less as Galileo discovered the laws of freely falling bodies. Imagine, then, that a scientist has "isolated" pairs of physical objects from all others; that he has hit upon the mass notion; and that by systematically varying the masses and the initial distances of his experimental pairs he has discovered N_2 or, as I shall also call it, the two-body law. N_2, we notice in passing, is the form the Newtonian equations themselves take in the case of two bodies, not their solution; for it states rates of change at a moment (specifically, the rate of change of velocity, i.e., the rate of change of the rate of change of position, which latter rate is a state variable) as functions of (some of) the relevant variables. Their solution, the (P) of the case, with which we need not bother, represents the two orbits, that is, the successive positions and velocities of the two bodies as functions of the relevant variables (i.e., their masses and their initial positions and velocities) and of the time lapsed. But let us return to the scientist of our fairy tale. Having discovered N_2, he begins a series of experiments with triples of "isolated bodies," hoping to discover N_3, the three-body law which states the accelerations at a moment of three bodies "in isolation" as functions of their masses and mutual distances at this moment. We may imagine that our scientist is again fortunate enough to discover N_3 by "direct" experimentation. Nor does his luck run out. He continues his experiments and discovers successively N_4, N_5, and so on, up to, say, N_{100}. Then he tires of the drudgery, quits his laboratory, and resorts to paper and pencil. Before we join him in his study, we had better realize that though in principle they could, scientists do not in fact proceed in this manner, at least not when they can help it. To mistake the story for a picture of their routine is in its own way as unrealistic as the imaginary assumption concerning the direct demonstrability of Newtonian attraction among terrestrial objects. However, this is beside the point; or, rather, the artificiality will bring out the points I want to make.

I wrote N_2, but I have so far not written N_3, N_4, N_5, and so on. Now I shall state these many-body laws, though for simplicity's sake only in their geometrical version. Comparing N_2 and N_3 our scientist *discovers* that N_3 can be obtained from N_2 by a tripartite rule. The notation I use in stating it becomes obvious if one labels the three bodies 1, 2, 3 respectively and looks at Figure 5. (a) *Decompose* the initial state of the three-body

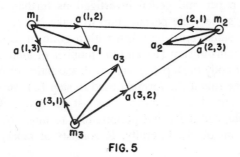

FIG. 5

system $(1, 2, 3)$ into the initial states of the three two-body systems $(1, 2)$, $(2, 3)$, $(3, 1)$ that are *contained* in it. (b) Compute for each of the three *imagined* two-body systems obtained in step (a) the accelerations each body *would* have according to N_2. The computation assigns to each body two imagined accelerations, e.g., to 1 the accelerations $a_1^{(1,2)}$ and $a_1^{(1,3)}$ from the imagined systems $(1, 2)$ and $(1, 3)$ respectively. (c) From the two accelerations assigned to each body in step (b) compute *according to a certain formula* a further acceleration for it. The computation yields three accelerations, a_1, a_2, a_3, the first a certain function of $a_1^{(1,2)}$ and $a_1^{(1,3)}$, the second and the third the same function of $a_2^{(2,1)}$, $a_2^{(2,3)}$ and $a_3^{(3,1)}$, $a_3^{(3,2)}$ respectively. To write down economically the "certain formula" (or, what amounts to the same thing, the "certain function") one must have some elementary notions about vectors. Fortunately the geometrical equivalent of the computation is familiar to every schoolboy. a_1 is the diagonal of the parallelogram whose sides are $a_1^{(1,2)}$ and $a_1^{(1,3)}$; a_2 is the diagonal of the parallelogram whose sides are $a_2^{(2,1)}$ and $a_2^{(2,3)}$; a_3 is the diagonal of the parallelogram whose sides are $a_3^{(3,1)}$ and $a_3^{(3,2)}$. These are the three parts or steps of the rule. *The three accelerations a_1, a_2, a_3 are those assigned to the three bodies by* N_3. This is the sense in which N_3 can be made or obtained from N_2 by the rule.

Having discovered this relation between N_3 and N_2, or, as I just put it, this way of *making* N_3 out of N_2, our scientist looks for ways of making N_4. The rule he eventually discovers is very similar to the one stated in the last paragraph. Thus a few words about each of its three parts will suffice. (a) prescribes decomposition into all the six possible imagined two-body systems, $(1, 2)$, $(2, 3)$, $(3, 4)$, $(4, 1)$, $(1, 3)$, $(2, 4)$. (b) assigns to each of the four bodies three imagined accelerations, one for each of the three imagined two-body systems to which it belongs. The formula used in the third step (c) for computing, say, a_1 from $a_1^{(1,2)}$, $a_1^{(1,3)}$, $a_1^{(1,4)}$ is analogous to the formula mentioned in the last paragraph, which is there used to compute a_1 from $a_1^{(1,2)}$ and $a_1^{(1,3)}$, in exactly the same sense in which, say, the product or the sum of three numbers is analogous to the product or the sum of two. It is, as one says, the same function, only with a different number of variables.

Pursuing his paper and pencil investigations further, our scientist discovers that the "same" rule permits him to make N_4, N_5 and so on, up to N_{100} out of N_2. 'Same' must be taken with a grain of salt. The number of imagined subsystems in step (a) and the number of imagined accelerations assigned to each body in step (b) vary with the index of N. Nor would we speak of the same rule if the formula used in step (c) were not the "same" in the sense explained at the end of the last paragraph. Our scientist has thus found a rule, call it R, that permits him to make N_3, N_4, N_5, and so on, up to N_{100} out of N_2. Literally, R consists of ninety-eight rules. But since all these rules are the "same" in a sense I have sufficiently explained, there is no danger of confusion in speaking of them as one rule. Nor is this all. R is quite easily stated for the "general case," that is, it is quite easy to replace in the statement of R the number of bodies by a letter, say, k, with the understanding that N_k becomes the law for systems with a specific number of bodies if k is replaced by this specific number. Suppose now that our scientist replaces k by a number greater than 100, say, 697, thus obtaining N_{697}. Not having experimented with systems of more than a hundred bodies, he does not have the same sort of evidence that N_{697} actually is the law for systems of six hundred ninety-seven bodies that he has for systems consisting of not more than a hundred bodies; for in the case of the latter and only in the case of the latter his inductive generalization was based on what I called direct experimental demonstration. But he will of course make the *inductive generalization,* not only for N_{697} but for any k, that N_k is the law of the k-body system, which law, if he wished, he could demonstrate directly.

This is the end of the story. Its lesson is clear. The two-body system is what I called an elementary system; N_2 is its process law. R is what I called a composition law. Like all such laws it has three parts. The first, (a), specifies how any system, Σ, is decomposed into imagined elementary systems. The second, (b), specifies the characters of the imagined elementary systems to be computed by means of the laws of the elementary processes. These laws make up one of the two classes of axioms of a process theory. The other class is the composition law or laws. There can of course be more than one such law (leaving aside the moot question we encountered a while ago, what is one law and what is two or more) according to what the result of (a) is and which characters of Σ are being computed. This computation is specified in the third part, (c), which states how to obtain the process law for Σ from the results of (b). Sometimes we speak and think as if (c) by itself were the composition law. For the most part no harm is done. For our purposes, though, we must grasp firmly that if a composition law is fully stated, it always consists of three parts corresponding to (a), (b), and (c) respectively. Point mechanics is merely an example. Yet the description of a composition law I just gave mentions no specific feature of our paradigm. This shows again why logical analysis proceeds best by describing specific cases in its own peculiarly abstractive way. I consider, then, that by means of our paradigm (and the artificialities of the story) I have explicated the two related notions of an elementary system and a composition law. To complete the explication some further comments are needed. In telling the story I italicized certain words when I used them for the first time. I shall now arrange my further comments around these words, italicizing them again as we encounter them.

I said that our scientist *makes* N_k out of N_2 by means of R or, briefly, out of N_2 and R. Generally we make the laws of many different systems out of the relatively small number of composition rules and laws for the elementary systems. This is the answer to the question with which we started. We now understand accurately how the occurrence of at least one composition rule among the axioms of a theory increases its scope. Take again our paradigm. Since each individual N_k is a process law, it is so rich in content that without too much artificiality one can call it a miniature theory. To see that, one merely has to consider that by the proper choice of values for the relevant variables (masses, initial positions, and velocities) even the "simplest" of these laws, N_2, can be made to cover such "different" situations as free fall, planets, comets, and double stars. But the scope and economy of a theory that "makes" all N out of N_2 and R is incomparably greater. Such economy is an essential feature of science. Economy depends on the scope of theory. Scope in turn depends on the occurrence of composition laws among the axioms. 'Economy', by the way, is not a felicitous word; at least, the phrase 'economy of science' has been the source of many squabbles, none of them very interesting. The way I spoke, there should not be any doubt as to what I mean. So I shall not reopen those stale arguments.

In the first step, (a), we *decompose* the initial state of the system, thus obtaining the *imagined* initial states of the elementary systems *contained* in it. In the second step, (b), we compute (in our paradigm) the accelerations the bodies *would* have if those elementary systems were not merely imagined. What I wished to emphasize by using some of these terms, e.g., 'imagined', is that some others among them, e.g., 'decomposition' and 'contained', are used metaphorically. They are metaphorical because they refer to paper and pencil operations or, if I may so express myself, the "decomposition" takes place in our mind and in our mind only. If I look in the fairy tale world of my story at an "isolated" five-body system, I do not look at the (ten) two-body systems which it metaphorically "contains"; this for the very good reason that there is in fact not even a single "isolated" two-body system for me to look at. If this were always clearly understood, certain confusions could not arise. Because of these confusions the emphasis I now provide is useful.

I called composition laws *rules* and I shall continue to call them so, at least occasionally; for the word comes quite easily when we refer to this sort of law. Yet 'rule' is confusing. (That is why I used it deliberately in order to get this point out of the way.) The source of the confusion is that 'rule' carries some of the connotations that are also carried by 'arbitrary', by 'convention', by 'way to proceed', and by 'man-made'. 'Law', used as in 'law of nature', has none of these connotations, a recent and right now very vociferous group of logical analysts to the contrary notwithstanding. A law states what is, or, if it is false, what is not the case.

It is therefore not arbitrary, man-made, or a convention. Nor is it a way to proceed; nor perhaps, as some believe, a rule for "inferring" a statement of individual fact from some other such statement or statements. To avoid this mistake, one merely has to remember that the law itself is one of the premisses of the inference (p. 76). A composition rule is a law; only it is a law of a peculiar kind. Its peculiarity is that it states how to "make" laws out of other laws. From 'making' a verbal bridge leads over 'way to proceed' to 'rule'. This is why 'rule' comes so readily out of our mouths when we speak of composition laws. (Notice that I used the imperative in stating R for the three-body problem.)

A composition law R, being a law, is synthetic. This is why I said that we *discover* it. The point is important and even crucial for at least three reasons. So I shall make sure that we understand it well before I state these reasons.

Nothing will be lost if we limit ourselves to N_2, N_3, and R. I said that one "makes" N_3 out of N_2 and R_3. This making is really a deducing. N_3 follows deductively from N_2 and R; it does not follow from N_2 alone; hence R is not a tautology but has factual content. Why, then, use 'making' at all? Its virtue is that, like 'composition' in 'composition law', it draws attention to the peculiarity of R. Without N_2 it would be of no use whatsoever. Its only use is to serve, with the proper value of k, as an additional premiss for the deduction of N_k from N_2 or, if you please, for the making of N_k out of N_2. Thus one may be tempted to mistake R for a pattern of deductive inference or, even, for a logical truth. To see once more why this is a mistake, let us examine the use I made of 'discover'. The scientist in my story discovers N_2 and N_3 directly. The factual nature of such discovery is clear beyond the possibility of confusion. But if, after he has discovered N_2 and N_3, he "discovers" that N_3 follows deductively from N_2 and R_3, he makes, if I may so express myself, a mere paper and pencil discovery, just as he would if, presented with two sentences of the form 'p' and 'p and q' respectively, he "discovered" that the latter can be deduced from the former and the additional premiss 'q'. Such "backward guessing" of helpful premisses, which often plays a major role in theorizing, is a species of (factual) discovering. Yet there seems to be a blur, probably because of the verbal bridge that leads from 'paper and pencil' to 'logical'. To dissolve the blur one merely has to realize that to say 'p and q' follows deductively from 'p' and 'q' is not the same thing as to say that 'q' is a tautology.

One contributory cause of confusion concerning the nature of composition laws is probably the particular composition law of the paradigm which, as we know, was very influential in forming our ideas. Speaking as the tongue runs, all of us, with the possible exception of a few hardy professional logicians, use 'logical' as an honorific interjection. Someone says something that is either very simple or very plausible, or with which we are very familiar. We exclaim, perhaps with a trace of impatience: "That's logical." Yet the statement made was synthetic. Newton's composition law is "logical" in this specious sense. Two of its features increase the illusion. For one thing, (a) specifies that the system be decomposed into "all possible" two-body systems. From 'all possible' a verbal bridge leads over 'all logically possible' to 'logical'. Yet there is really no "reason" or "necessity" why (a) should not prescribe that we first order the bodies by the magnitude of their masses and then decompose the system into the two-body systems consisting of the largest and the second largest, the second largest and the third largest, and so on. (This particular (a) must be supplemented by a proviso for the case of equal masses. The reader may amuse himself by inventing one.) For another thing, Newton's composition rule is also known as vector addition. The middle pillar of the verbal bridge that leads from 'addition' to 'logic' is 'arithmetic'. Of this presently, in one of the later sections, in connection with 'additivity'.

There are, I said, three reasons why it is important to realize that composition laws are synthetic. I am now ready to state them.

1. Whether a synthetic statement is true depends on what is the case. A composition law is a synthetic statement. Hence, whether or not there are (true) composition laws is a matter of fact. There is no "necessity" or "reason" for there being any. The analyst who clarifies their role does therefore not support the thesis (in the sense in which "determinism" and "relative chance" are theses) that there must be composition laws. All he can say as an analyst is, first, that scientists have in fact discovered some and, second, that science would be very different from what it actually is if there were none.

2. Toward the end of the story, when our scientist "extended" R to systems with more than a hundred bodies, I underlined the phrase *inductive generalization*. 'Inductive generalization' is really redundant; but redundancy is sometimes emphatic. What I wish to emphasize is best brought out by an appendix to the story. Imagine that further experimentation proves the generalization in question successful for quite some time until some day scientists must for some purpose deal with a system of a thousand bodies. Rather to their surprise, they find that N_{1000} is not the law of this particular process. Thereupon they engage in further systematic experimentation on the mutual attraction of bodies and discover that while R holds for $k < 1000$, it fails or, as I shall say, breaks down for $k \geqslant 1000$. The illustration is of course bizarre; the reader understands by now the method in this madness. In principle, though, there is nothing paradoxical about it, either logically or otherwise. There never is when a generalization is not borne out by new facts. The logic of this particular failure, the breakdown of a composition rule at a certain level of complexity, is so important

in the philosophy of the behavior sciences that I shall attend to it in a moment.

3. Since composition laws are synthetic statements of fact (once more, redundancy for the sake of emphasis!), it makes no sense to say that those who search for them and, if they believe they have found one, make the most of it (which is a good deal), are thereby committed to a certain "logic" or "philosophy" of science. Otherwise it would also make sense to say that one so commits himself if he insists, after he has discovered it, that water if heated boils. Yet such things have been said and are still being said in the philosophy of the behavior sciences. The idea is, as one would expect, that this particular "logic" or "philosophy" is inadequate. The (pejorative) adjectives that crop up most frequently in such discussions are 'elementaristic' and 'atomistic'. Their (honorific) opposites are 'organic' or 'organismic' and 'holistic'. Clearly, these are "philosophical" uses of 'element', 'atom', 'whole', 'organism', and their derivatives. So we must analyze them in order to dispose of them. A first installment of the analysis will be found at the end of the section.

This concludes the explication of 'composition law'. We understand that the composition laws of an otherwise successful theory *may* break down at a certain level of complexity. On the other hand, there is no reason to believe that the composition laws of, say, physics, actually will break down. Physicists at least do not think so. The logical analyst merely takes note of their opinion; he is not himself a forecaster on what are essentially matters of scientific judgment. His is a different task. Some argue, positively, that there *must* be composition laws that cannot break down. Some others argue, negatively, that whatever composition laws there are must break down at certain levels or, similarly, that there can be no such laws in certain areas. All these arguments use words "philosophically." Thus they are bad arguments. The analyst dissects them so that we may understand accurately where and why they err. Of course, their burden is not always stated explicitly. As I put it once before, had certain things been said clearly, they wouldn't have been said at all. Moreover, these arguments are confusedly and confusingly mingled with others, which I shall take up as we encounter them. The issue at hand is merely the (implicit or explicit) controversy about composition laws. I disposed of the arguments I just called positive by the very way I introduced the issue. Those I call negative have been very prominent and still are prominent, though perhaps to a lesser degree, in the philosophy of the behavior sciences. So we must examine them with some care. The best approach is to inquire what possibilities there are if a composition law breaks down. Let me then return to my counterfactual illustration, the breakdown of Newton's composition law for $k \geq 1000$.

One virtue of this bizarre example is that it shows very clearly what I mean by *level of complexity*. The phrase is woolly. Having used it only because I did not want to stop for explanations, I shall explain it now. Take a five-body system. It "contains" as "parts" five (imagined) four-body systems, ten (imagined) three-body systems, and ten (imagined) two-body systems. Since 'part' is a correlative of 'whole', I shall in the next section explicate it more formally. But there should be no doubt as to what I mean in this case, particularly in view of the added 'imagined'. If a system is in this sense a part of another, then the latter is more complex or of a higher level of complexity than the former.

If Newton's R broke down for $k = 1000$, there would be four possibilities. (1) All attempts to find a process law for $k = 1000$ having failed, we may conclude that there is none. This makes the level of breakdown the boundary of chance or, perhaps, if some statistical regularities can be discovered, of relative chance. (2) There is a process law for $k = 1000$, but it involves new characters (variables). To pile outlandishness upon outlandishness, imagine, for instance, that with this number of bodies some of their chemical properties become relevant for their motions. A "new" variable, then, is one of a kind that would not occur in any complete set of relevant variables of any system of lesser complexity. This alternative has an interesting variant, so-called "emergence," which I shall discuss in the next section. (3) There is a process law for thousand-body systems that involves no new variables but that cannot be made by a composition rule out of N_2. (4) There is a process law that involves no new variables and that can be made out of N_2 by means of a composition rule different from R. This new composition rule, call it R', may differ from R in any one of its three parts (a), (b), (c); or in any two of them; or in all three. (This is one occasion on which it is important to realize that every composition rule has three parts.) In this case one almost expects, though one can of course not be certain, that R' will also work for $k > 1000$, though perhaps only up to the next level of complexity, at which it will in turn break down. There is a related possibility for (2) and (3). It may be that if N_{1000} and a new composition rule R'' is added to the axioms of the original theory, the process laws for $k > 1000$ can be deduced. If a name were wanted, one could in this case speak of a two-level theory.

Two levels of alleged breakdown are of particular interest. The first supposedly divides nonliving from living matter; the second, mere living matter from living matter inhabited by minds or endowed with consciousness. I shall say a few words about the first, which does not specially concern us. A very detailed analysis of the second is, naturally, implicit in Volume Two. I say implicit because fortunately the issue need not be discussed in its misleading classical formulations. Some of the latter will command our attention only in Volume Three.

Assume that a scientist who studies living things uses only the terms of physics and chemistry. The full significance of this limitation on his vocabulary will be understood after the discussion of "reduction" in the last section of this chapter. As to the objects of the investigation, no matter how "simple" the animals and plants our scientist selects may be, the relative "complexity" of living matter makes it more than plausible that it is, with respect to systems of nonliving physical objects, on a level of greater complexity in the sense in which I have used the phrase in this discussion. (Complexity, in any sense, is of course not a matter of size.) To assert that in this case one of the possibilities (4) or (3) is realized, or even the nonemergentist variant of (2) which I have illustrated, is to maintain a perfectly "reasonable" version of *vitalism* (p. 107). At least, it is reasonable in that it leads to no logical difficulties. Nor does it present the analyst with any other challenge beyond the one just met, namely, to state clearly what is (would be) the case. That the overwhelming majority of biologists happen to disallow these possibilities is therefore nothing an analyst would get excited about.

Generally, (4), (3), and the nonemergentist variant of (2) are of no particular analytical interest. Even emergence is, as we shall presently see, a matter of fact, not of logic, though, to be sure, in a much more radical sense, so radical indeed that the analyst can hardly avoid joining the debate.

Having given the devil his due by stating a reasonable version of vitalism, I shall make use of it to explain why most of the "holistic" arguments against composition laws, those I called negative, are confused, mixed with others, and altogether anything but reasonable. (4), (3), and the nonemergentist variant of (2) are compatible with the thesis of determinism. So is, strictly speaking, the other variant of (2), though determinism certainly "takes the fun out it." This is just the point. The intellectual motive behind those arguments is, once more, concern for freedom and the wish, which so often goes with it, to "refute" determinism on "philosophical" grounds. If one is in this frame of mind and accepts certain specious premises, then one ought to argue for (1). But (1) is a bit barefaced. There "should" be another kind of lawfulness, so-called teleological lawfulness, making possible a world comprehensively lawful and yet not "deterministic." As it happens and as we shall see in Volume Two, this notion of teleological lawfulness does not bear examination in the light of logic (not of fact!). The fog through which one can continue to behold it hopefully rises from arguments that zigzag ambiguously and elusively, without ever really committing themselves, among (1), the two variants of (2), (3), and (4). Their typical admixtures are taken from the arguments that have grown around 'purpose' and 'meaning'. Who saves "meaning" saves "freedom"; and "meaning" resides in the "whole." This is one of the major patterns of a certain superficial dialectic that has long been very powerful in our tradition. We shall find it in Dewey as well as in the Gestaltists, particularly, with remarkable explicitness, in Wertheimer.

So much for the thing, composition laws; now for some words. 'Atomistic' is used in the analysis of physical theories; 'elementaristic' is rather useful in the logical analysis of classical introspectionism. Outside of these two special areas one could do very well without either of these two words. Probably the philosophy of science would be better off if neither had been used "philosophically." But since they have in fact been so used and still are so used, particularly in the philosophy of the behavior sciences, we cannot afford to ignore them. Scientists search for and expect to find composition laws. This is but another aspect of their Newtonian frame of reference. If 'elementarism' or 'atomism' are to be used at all, one may use them to refer to this feature of our frame of reference. Theories that contain composition rules will then be called 'atomistic' or 'elementaristic'. Again, I am not recommending this use of the terms; I just said that I could get along without them. The point is, rather, that this is the only clear and specific meaning that could be attributed to them (outside of the two special areas I just mentioned) in the philosophy of any science. Their "philosophical" use, without any clear and specific meanings, by the Gestaltists and other "holists" is the source of at least three confusions. *First,* they are used to create the impression that there are viable alternatives for the construction of theories of some scope. Yet all known theories are in fact elementaristic (I am now using the word with the meaning I gave to it) and we cannot even think of any other way to attain scope. *Second,* these words occur at crucial places in arguments to the effect that elementarism (in some philosophical sense) is a special "philosophy" or "logic" of science rather than a feature (in the sense I gave it) of science itself (p. 139). This mistake then serves as basis for the claim that, *third,* "elementaristic" theories cannot, on purely philosophical or even logical grounds, account for the characteristics of "wholes."

'Whole' and 'additive' are probably the most misused and, for some, the most magic in the group of related words whose explication is one of the tasks I set myself in this chapter. Nor is this particular task unimportant in view of what is still being said and written. As always, the explications of such a group of words depend on and supplement each other, which complicates the exposition. 'Additive', for instance, I had better save for later. To 'whole' I shall have to return. But I am ready to state the only two clear meanings of the term.

In its first good meaning, "whole" is synonymous with 'system of interaction'. In this sense every system, in the precise sense of 'system' which we established in the second chapter, is a whole, though it may of course contain two or more closed subsystems or, if you please, subwholes. Take then the statement I just attributed to advocates of "holism": (1) An elementaristic theory cannot account for the characteristics of wholes. As they are used in these arguments, the two phrases 'an elementaristic theory' and 'characteristics of the whole' are hopelessly vague. Replace the first by 'a theory containing composition rules'; the second, by 'the characteristics of a system of interaction' or, briefly, by 'interaction'. Now the sentence reads: (2) Theories containing composition rules cannot account for interaction. Whoever has understood what has been said so far immediately recognizes (2) for a falsehood. Yet (1) is still being reiterated over and over again, literally and in all sorts of disguises. This shows once more what comes from using words "philosophically." The particular point is so important that I shall repeat it presently, in the context of 'additivity' and 'configuration'. As I just hinted, a measure of repetition is unavoidable in this analysis; nor will it hurt; certain thought patterns are too deeply engrained for that.

The second good meaning of 'whole' is much narrower. In this sense, I would call a thousand-body system a whole if and only if N_2 and R broke down for it. Generally, a system is a whole in the second sense if and only if the composition rules that hold for its "parts" fail for it. Clearly, a whole in the first sense need not be a whole in the second sense. It is indeed very doubtful, to say the least, whether there are any wholes in this second, narrower sense. The notion is nonetheless analytically interesting; and 'whole' suggests itself quite naturally as a name for this (possible) kind of system. As far as I can see, this is indeed the only worthwhile technical use to which the idiomatic 'whole' could be put. For to introduce 'whole' (in the first and wider sense) as a synonym for 'system of interaction' serves no purpose and is merely confusing.

The second, narrow meaning of 'whole' is synonymous with the meaning 'organism' seems to have when it is used "philosophically." Here is another source of confusion. For in its other meaning, the ordinary meaning with which biologists use it, 'organism' is quite unproblematic. There is therefore no need to explicate this ordinary meaning. The point is, rather, that biologists overwhelmingly reject the claim that "organisms" in the ordinary sense are also "organisms" in the philosophical sense, which is synonymous with the narrower sense of 'whole'. 'Organism' is thus another word with at least two meanings. As always, the ambiguity invites specious arguments of the kind I call verbal bridges. This particular bridge is reinforced by the verbal habit of treating 'organismic' and 'mechanistic' as opposites; which fits nicely with the tendency to use 'mechanistic' as if it were synonymous with 'elementaristic' and 'atomistic'. I say as if it were synonymous because I hesitate to suggest clear meanings where there are none. The specious conclusion to which we are led over the bridge is, as one would expect, that any science dealing with "organisms" couldn't possibly be of the same logical structure as "mechanics." The thesis remains unsupported. Yet it is worth reflecting on how tight and in all its untidiness even tidy the verbal bridge is. 'Additive', we shall see, provides another of its reinforcers. (Incidentally, I omitted this particular meaning of 'mechanistic', identical with the one I gave to 'elementaristic', from the little glossary on the word I inserted earlier (p. 107). The reason is that it is rather close to the third one, (c), which I listed.)

CONFIGURATIONS: DESCRIPTION

'Configuration', like 'form', 'structure', and some other words, has long lost all specific meaning. These words serve merely as a sort of filler, satisfying the grammatical need for a subject, or an object, or what not. On ordinary occasions the context reveals what they stand for, so their desperate generality does no harm. For such purposes 'configuration' is probably interchangeable with 'pattern' or 'arrangement' and, perhaps, even with 'structure' or 'form'. 'Configuration' is also the most widely current English equivalent of *'Gestalt'*, quite properly, for the German word, too, is merely a filler, as may be seen from the fact that its most literal translation is 'shape'. Now a filler word may be rehabilitated by assigning to it a specific technical meaning. Trouble brews only if the talk purporting to do that is "philosophical." This is the case with 'configuration' which I, too, shall use as the equivalent of 'Gestalt'. Configurations, in the view of the classical configurationists (Gestaltists) and not in theirs alone, are wholes. This provides for another fateful verbal bridge. It is so well-trodden that my best plan is to follow it, not in my thought, to be sure, but in my exposition. Both 'configuration' and 'whole' are used in two contexts. As their context shifts, so does their meaning. Much of the blur which surrounds them is due to these shifts, whether inadvertent or intentional is beside the point. (This is one reason, though not the only one, why I devoted a whole section to the distinction between description and explanation.) The two clear meanings of 'whole' which I explicated in the last section belong unmistakably to the context of explanation. Yet the idea of "configurations" arose, with Wertheimer, in the context of description. The particular flavor of the German word helped, in the German literature, to mask the shift. This is one strand of the dialectic. Another is more subtle. Presently we shall see that 'whole' has a third articulate meaning, which does belong to the context of description. This meaning, though, is rather esoteric; wholes in this sense would be exemplified only if the emergentist possibility were realized. And emergentism is hardly more than a bare possibility, or, to say the same thing more suggestively, the emergentists describe a possible world which, as it happens, is almost certainly not ours. Interestingly, Wertheimer rejects emergentism, which leaves him without a specific and clear meaning of 'whole' or *'Gestalt'* in the context of description. The one he clings to is specious, an illusion one can maintain only by confusing the two contexts. This confusion I shall analyze in the next section. In this section I intend to raise and answer some questions about descriptions. This bit of analysis is not only of some moderate interest in itself; it is also an indispensable part of the analysis whose major outlines I just drew in order to provide some preliminary orientation. The actual explications will take some care and, therefore, some time.

Since my intent is not polemical, I rarely identify the arguments which I critically examine. Thus one may think that I am singling out the pragmatists and the Gestaltists, and among them Dewey and Wertheimer in particular. Not at all. Since every likely reader of this book associates certain thought patterns, or even certain words, with these names, it would be very artificial or, even worse, it would be coy not to mention them occasionally. As to the thought patterns themselves, they are very influential and very widely spread, far beyond the group of self-conscious pragmatists and Gestaltists, in the philosophy of the behavior sciences. They always were very influential in our tradition (the names of Plato and Hegel come to mind). Dewey and Wertheimer merely adapted them, very effectively, to the scientific and analytic climate of the recent past.

Two analysts, Grelling and Oppenheim, were the first to distinguish the two contexts in the analysis of '*Gestalt*'. Their terms are '*W-Gestalt*' and '*K-Gestalt*' for the contexts of description and explanation respectively. The letters are taken from 'Wertheimer' and 'Koehler', quite aptly, I think, since Koehler wanted above all to emphasize interaction, while Wertheimer's main concern, however confusedly, was description. (Grelling perished in the slaughterhouses of the Nazis.)

Wertheimer's rejection of vitalism and emergentism fits with what I said before, when I tried to explain the characteristic elusiveness of the holistic arguments (p. 141). The dominant motive, whether conscious or unconscious, is to enjoy the consolations, with respect to "freedom," "meaning," and so on, of certain less plausible positions without committing one's self to them. At least Wertheimer was consistent; he did not shrink from the conclusion that even "mechanics" is not really "mechanistic" and that Newton and "traditional" logic (which includes, in ordinary parlance, modern logic) are all a mistake. So we may salute his courage.

Imagine that we are presented with three test tubes, number them 1, 2, 3, each containing a single chemical, call them A, B, C. Nothing happens in any of the tubes; the chemicals are, as one says, stable (under the prevailing conditions of pressure, temperature, etc.). Call the three statements that describe the content of the tubes D_1, D_2, D_3. One reason I use 'D' rather than 'C' or 'S', as I did in the analysis of process, is that D may, and as a rule will, contain statements from what I then called the S-bracket as well as from the C-bracket. Notice, on the other hand, that I omitted the superscript which I added to S in order to indicate the moment t at which the system is in the state S^t describes. Take now a fourth, empty tube and pour into it part of the contents of 1 as well as the contents of 2. Take still another tube, the fifth; pour into it the rest of the contents of 1 as well as the contents of 3. The contents of each of these two tubes can, and for certain purposes must, be described. Call these descriptions $D_{1,2}$

and $D_{1,3}$ respectively. (I am not yet considering the relations among, say, $D_{1,2}$ and D_1 and D_2.) Imagine that nothing happens in the fourth tube or, as one says, that chemicals A and B do not react with each other (under the prevailing temperature, pressure, concentration, etc.). In the fifth tube, a rather lively reaction between chemicals A and C starts immediately and continues for some time. As we more broadly use 'describe' when we speak as we ordinarily do, we may "describe" this process. As I more narrowly use 'describe', we pass, when we do that, from the context of description to that of explanation. If 'describe' is to be used at all, one would have to say that in describing (in the narrower sense, as I use the word) the contents of the tube at successive (selected) moments, we "describe" (in the broader sense, as I don't use the word) the reaction or "process" that takes place in it. (I quarantined 'process' between quotation marks because, so used, it carries at most a hint at a process law.) But, then, each of these descriptions will have to be provided with a superscript to indicate the moment at which the test tube has this content. The $D_{1,3}$ I mentioned before is the $D_{1,3}{}^0$; time being counted from the moment the two chemicals have been poured into the tube. Strictly speaking, $D_{1,2}$, too, should be written $D_{1,2}{}^0$. Only, since "nothing happens" in this tube, we can without danger of confusion suppress the superscript. In the terms of this story, questions about description are all about $D_{1,2}{}^0$ and $D_{1,3}{}^0$, not about the processes which what they describe may or may not undergo. The example shows, as clearly as only an example can, the difference between the two contexts.

There is still another reason for using 'D' rather than 'C' or 'S'. It will be remembered that I had some trouble with 'system' in the analysis of process. As I proposed to use the term, strictly, a system is the system of a process, that is, what is described by a C-bracket and, at any given moment, by an S-bracket such that there is also a (P) all of whose relevant variables the two brackets specify. This left me without a convenient word for what other descriptions refer to. Occasionally I used 'system' broadly; when there was reason to be careful, I spoke of groups of physical objects and the characters, including relational ones, they exemplify. From now on I shall use 'configuration' to refer to such "groups"; and, needless to add, I shall not use it in any other sense. Whether we say that two configurations are the "same" may depend on how far we have pushed their descriptions. If this is not immediately clear to the reader, it will become so if he re-reads the discussion of 'same' in connection with 'system' (p. 98). In a similar vein, it makes no sense to say without qualification that a description is complete or exhaustive. The only sense it could make, a listing of "all" characters exemplified in the configuration, is both elusive and difficult. It is also thoroughly impractical. One describes configurations in such detail as one needs or thinks one needs; they are needed to serve as additional premisses to laws. Whether a description is complete or exhaustive in this relative sense depends on the law one expects to apply. E.g., a description of a group of rigid bodies sufficiently complete to predict their gravitational motions would not need to mention any of their chemical characteristics; thus it would not be an adequate additional premiss for a law predicting the chemical reactions between any two of the bodies in case they collide in the course of their gravitational motions.

Consider once more the case of the fifth tube, whose contents (at the start of the reaction) are described by $D_{1,3}$ (I suppress the superscript 0). Without prejudging any of the questions one may raise about what $D_{1,3}$ does or does not mention, we may assume that it mentions how many grams of each of the two chemicals A and C the tube contains without mentioning the ratio of these two numbers. As it happens, the speed of the reaction that is about to take place in the tube depends in many cases very markedly on just this ratio. It does not follow that the ensuing reaction therefore cannot in all detail be predicated from $D_{1,3}$ (in conjunction with the process law of the reaction). Obviously, it can; for if $D_{1,3}$ tells us what the two masses are, as by assumption it does, we can ourselves compute their ratio which, again by assumption, $D_{1,3}$ does not tell us. The following psychological illustration exemplifies the same pattern. A psychologist who sets out to investigate the processes (explanation!) involving people's responses to musical chords will soon discover that some of these responses depend, not on the frequencies of the tones (which I assume for simplicity's sake to be pure), but on the ratios of these frequencies (the musical intervals). If these ratios were the only cues on which the response depends, descriptions of chords mentioning only the frequencies of the tones which make them up would still serve our investigator's purpose. For he can again easily compute the ratios. The generalization from the examples is not difficult. If given a description of a configuration, one is *implicitly* also given all those of its characters (in the quantified case, values of variables) that are definable in terms of the characters (variables) the description *explicitly* mentions.

So far we have merely disposed of the fairly obvious. The questions the "holists" raised about configurations go deeper. (That they handled these questions badly because they confused the two contexts is beside the point.) At least, they go so deep that we shall have to pay more explicit attention to language than we have paid for some time. In order to clarify what is being said about "wholes" and "parts," we must examine their respective descriptions, the logical structure of these descriptions, and the logical relations among them.

Etymologically, 'configuration' suggests a measure of complexity, or structure, or pattern, choose whichever filler word you prefer. The configurations we are interested in, in science and in our everyday pursuits, are indeed more or less "complex." Trying to assign a specific meaning to the filler 'complex' in this context, we reap the first benefit of the linguistic turn I am about to take. A configuration is more complex than another if the description of the former is a "longer" statement than that of the latter. Strictly, complexity thus depends on how far we push the description; but I have said what needs to be said on this score once and for all. The important question now is how to compare the "lengths" of descriptions.

How "long" a description is depends not only on what it is about but also on the language in which it is stated. Remember the distinction between "realistic" and "phenomenalistic" languages (p. 40). 'Stone' could be an undefined predicate of a "realistic" language. If so, then 'This is a stone' is a very "short" statement of such a language; it is even atomic (p. 41). To state the same thing (in some sense of 'same') in a "phenomenalistic" language requires a very "long" statement. I stipulate, then, that our descriptions are stated in a "realistic" language. (That is merely a reminder of a stipulation made before for the whole of this book.) This is the *first* step in the explication of 'length', as applied to descriptions. If a defined term is eliminated from a statement by means of its definition, the resulting statement will as a rule be "longer." I stipulate, therefore, that in our descriptions all defined terms have been eliminated. This is the *second* step. When we distinguished between description and explanation in the first section of the last chapter, we discovered that a description does not contain the logical operators. Or, to put the same thing differently, a description must not contain a statement of lawfulness. Thus it is either an atomic statement or compounded from such statements by means of logical connectives; such as, for instance, 'This is green *and* this is square *and* that is red *and* that is round *and* this is to the left of that', which may pass for the description of a configuration consisting of a green square and a red circle, the former to the left of the latter. Furthermore, a description is always a conjunction. We remember that 'p and q', or, as I shall sometimes write, 'p & q' is the form of a conjunction with two (conjunctive) constituents; 'p & q & r' the form of one with three; our example has five conjunctive constituents; I italicized the four 'and'. Upon a little reflection it becomes obvious that all descriptions must be of this form. If something is "complex," then we must in order to describe it make more than one assertion about it. Clearly, we mean each of these assertions to be true; and the form our language provides for joint assertion is conjunction. We are ready for a *third* step. The length of a description is the maximum number of conjunctive constituents into which it can be decomposed.

This explication of 'length' employs only syntactical notions. Thus it can be transferred from a "realistic" to a "phenomenalistic" or any other language. This shows that our analysis of 'configuration' is in no way limited by the "realistic" mode of its presentation. Whatever differences there are between configurations of "physical" and of "mental" things can only be a matter of the laws that apply to these two sorts of things. Thus they belong to the context of explanation.

Concerning the first step. There is now again much argument among analysts as to whether there is any sense in which a statement *P* of a "phenomenalistic" language could state what is stated by such statements of a "realistic" language as 'This is a stone'. Fortunately everybody agrees on two things. 1. *P* would not only be very "long"; it would also contain operators. (Our explication of 'length' would have to be supplemented for statements that contain operators.) 2. *P* "reconstructs" such statements as 'This is a stone' only schematically. Agreement on 2 limits disagreement to an issue which, as we saw, is also at the core of other current controversies, namely, the usefulness of mere "schemata" in logical analysis. I shall have to say a little more about the question of a "phenomenalistic reconstruction" in Volume Two. Even there, though, I shall not analyze it as closely as it would have to be analyzed if this were a work on philosophy proper.

Concerning the second step. The definientia of many definitions do in fact contain operators. A description that contains a term so defined is, strictly speaking, no longer a description. It is not necessary, though, to cut it that fine either for the purposes of science or, for the most part, even of its philosophy. The analyst must of course attend to these subtleties. How much space he will give to them is a matter of taste and judgment. I prefer to take them up once and for all, in the context in which they matter most, as I did in this case when I devoted a whole section to the distinction between description and explanation. (Remember the piece of "wax.")

Concerning the third step. A minimal conjunctive constituent of the description of a configuration need not be atomic. If, for instance, such a constituent ascribes to an object a dispositional property, then it will, in the simplest case, be of the form 'if *p* then *q*', where '*p*' and '*q*' both stand for atomic sentences.

I am ready for four clarifications which together comprehend one-half of what needs to be said about configurations. *First.* The description of a configuration is never a single atomic statement but always a conjunction each of whose constituents may or may not be atomic. This guarantees in a minimal fashion the "complexity" we want to suggest by calling something a configuration. *Second.* Practically, and certainly in all those cases which preoccupy the "holists," at least one of the atomic constituents of the description of a configuration is a relational statement. In the example I just gave, the green square to the left of the red circle, the relational constituent is 'This is to the left of that'. This is another aspect of the "complexity" of configurations. *Third.* 'And-connection' is a natural synonym of 'conjunction'. According to the "holist," the "elementarist's" fundamental shortcoming is that he treats configurations (wholes, *Gestalten*) as *"Undverbindungen."* The word is Wertheimer's; its literal translation is 'and-connection'. The description of a configuration is indeed always an and-connection; but to say that the configuration itself is one is simply non-sense, just as it would be nonsense to say that a chair is a noun because, as it happens, 'chair' is a noun; for it patently makes no sense to ascribe linguistic (syntactical) properties to things nonlinguistic. Thus, since the indictment makes no sense, the so-called "elementarists" could not pos-sibly be guilty. (I shall return to the point presently, in the analysis of 'additivity'.)

Fourth. We can now explicate the relevant meanings of 'part'. There is (a) a descriptive meaning. In this sense, some physical objects are parts of others; a branch is part of a tree; the limbs or, for that matter, any group of their cells, are parts of a human body. I shall not bother to ex-plicate this meaning. There is (b) another descriptive meaning. In this sense a configuration is a part of another if it has actually been made out of the latter by actually removing some of the objects mentioned in the description. I emphasize 'actually' for the same reason I emphasized 'imagined' earlier (p. 136). If in my last fairy tale we actually remove one of the bodies of a three-body configuration so that what remains is an "isolated" two-body configuration, then the latter is a part in sense (b), and not merely an imagined part, of the original configuration. For another example, consider my body as a configuration. Its limbs are parts of it in sense (a). If they were severed from it, they would for all practical pur-poses also become parts of it in sense (b). That they would wither and that the torso might die are matters of process (explanation) and therefore beside the point. Finally, in a logical sense (c) a description, D_1, may be called part of another, D_2, if and only if D_2 is a conjunction of D_1 and some further statements. (Each conjunctive constituent of D_1 is one of D_2, but not conversely.) The meanings (b) and (c) need not always corre-spond; a description of a part in sense (b) need not be a part in sense (c) of the description of the original configuration; for the description of the part, in sense (b), could be made more detailed than it had been before the part was severed. Also, whenever the description of a configuration is pushed further without removing anything from it, the less "complete" one is a part of the more "complete." Idiomatically, 'whole' is a correlative of 'part'. Precisely, a configuration may be called a whole relative to any of its parts in sense (a) or in sense (b) or, even, relative to any of its imagined parts. This is one possible meaning of 'whole' in the context of description. So used, the word is not much more than a filler; what is worse, it has become a source of confusion by being blurred into other meanings of 'whole'. (I shall give a glossary of all possible meanings of 'whole' in the next section.)

So much for one-half of the explication of 'configuration'. The other half, to which I now turn, consists of an examination of the characters, including relational ones, exemplified by a configuration as such, that is, not by any of the objects mentioned in its description or by any of its parts (in the appropriate meaning or meanings of 'part', which I shall no longer bother to specify). In the course of this examination we shall encounter a possibility that suggests a natural and useful service for 'whole'. As I hinted in my preliminary remarks, this is the one worthwhile meaning of 'whole' in the context of description. But I also hinted that this possibility is a mere possibility. There are no configurations that are wholes in this particular sense of 'whole'. That there are none is a matter of fact, though of such a kind that the analyst could not and should not keep out of the controversies that have long swirled around it. This, too, I indicated before. But even here not everything is controversial. So I shall begin with what is not.

Take a cube made out of metal rods with bolts and nuts. Obviously it can be looked at as a configuration. Obviously it both makes sense and is true to say that "it" is a cube. Equally obviously, it is false to say this of any of its parts or of any of the individual rods, nuts, or bolts. There are thus characters exemplified by configurations and only by configurations "as such." (The example clarifies incidentally how I use the often spurious phrase 'as such'.) This particular character, though, can be defined. Everybody agrees that (the names of) *some* characters exemplified by configurations as such can be defined in terms of others. The question is whether *all* can. This is the issue. The proponents of *emergentism* take the negative. I shall, in my own cautious way, take the positive. More important, we shall see once more that whatever may be the judgment one must eventually make, careful analysis in itself, by removing smoke-screen issues, greatly reduces the heat of controversy. Take 'purposive'. As we ordinarily use them, 'purpose' and 'purposive' apply both to mental and to physical things. My concern here is only with the latter use. We all know roughly what it means to say that organisms (ordinary meaning!) are purposive. There is no disagreement on that. (The phrase is not very idiomatic. More smoothly, we would rather say that an organism displays or is capable of displaying purposive behavior. The roughness is without significance. Besides, it will be seen in a moment that the smoother phrase favors my own judgment.) Furthermore, we all agree that at least the higher animals are in fact purposive. There is no disagreement on that either. The only issue is whether 'purposive' can be defined, e.g., as a dispositional character, namely, as the (name of the) disposition to display under certain circumstances certain kinds of behavior; these circumstances and these behaviors to be described without the use of either 'purposive' or one of its cognates. The smoke-screen issue is created by giving the impression that those who take (in this case) the antiemergentist stand "deny the existence of purpose." Taking the phrase as we do when we speak as the tongue runs, I would no more deny the existence of purpose than I would deny that fire burns or that water wets.

I interrupt for two incidental remarks. For one thing, we understand now how emergentism has come by its name. What "emerges" are the allegedly undefinable characters of certain configurations. Configurations that exemplify such characters one might quite reasonably call 'wholes'. This is, finally, that one significant meaning of 'whole' in the context of description of which I have spoken for some time. However, this is only one of the two variants of emergentism; I shall call it the *nonsubstantialist* variant. What suggests the name will be understood after we have, at the end of the section, examined the *substantialist* variant of emergentism. For another thing, I want to address once more those readers who are dismayed by finding so much philosophy and so little behavior science in this first part of a work on the philosophy of the behavior sciences. The example I just chose, partly for this very reason, should encourage them. The analysis of such notions as 'purpose' is one of the main topics of Volume Two. The analysis of 'purpose' itself is one of the keys to the understanding of Mac-Dougall. Thus, since the latter was a rather important figure, we shall have to make use of it also in Volume Three. Nor is this all. Among the things that emerge according to the substantialist variant of emergentism are, in one subvariant, minds, in the other subvariant, mental contents. (The difference between these two subvariants will concern us only in Volume Three.) But it is abundantly clear that we must secure a firm foundation for the discussion of all these issues. There is only one way to do that. One must, without paying too much attention to any one of them, examine the fundamental logic that underlies all of them.

I return to the thesis of nonsubstantialist emergentism. Let me first state it, in three propositions, as clearly as we now can. (1) The *undefined* character words of any *adequate improved language* fall into groups, G^1, G^2, G^3, and so on; how many such groups there are is, relatively speaking, a matter of detail. (2) Each group G^i consists of two subgroups, call them G_k^i and G_p^i; the members of G_k^i are the names of kinds of either physical objects or configurations of such; the members of G_p^i are the names of other characters of either physical objects or configurations of such. (3) No character mentioned in any G_p is exemplified by any instance of a kind mentioned in any G_k with a lower upper index. (3) is of course the heart of the matter. We see now that the emergentist makes a factual statement of that peculiarly broad kind we have encountered on earlier occasions. (I am thus consistent in my use of 'thesis' when I call emergentism a "thesis.") As on all such occasions, we cannot do without the analyst. Here are some of the reasons why his services are required in this case. When we speak as we ordinarily do, either in science or in everyday life, we do not define all the words that could be defined, either in sufficient detail or in principle. This is why I underlined the phrase 'adequate improved language' in (1). Omit it and nothing is left to talk about. Include it and you see that you must first inform yourself about the nature and purpose of those peculiar languages. This information only the analyst can give you. I tried to provide a minimum of it in the first chapter. As a result, we understand the importance of the distinction I just mentioned between definability in principle and in satisfactory detail. It splits the evaluation of the emergentist thesis into two parts. (a) If scientifically accurate definitions are demanded, then the thesis will, like all such theses, remain undecided or "open" for ever, in exactly the same sense in which science itself is and, to the best of our knowledge, always will be "open." (b) If emergence is argued "philosophically," as in fact it is, then definition in principle suffices. For the behavior sciences, we shall play this game, explicitly and implicitly, in Volume Two. It will furnish us with what I consider excellent grounds for the judgment that the emergentist claim is unsound.

The case of emergentist holism supports the generalization that such "theses" should not be argued "directly." Here are two further reasons why this is so in the case at hand.

1. What "emerges" in the substantialist variant is, as I mentioned before, minds or mental contents. One intellectual motive behind this is to assure one's self "philosophically" that minds (or mental contents) exist. Now, if you take the phrase as we do when we speak as we ordinarily do, then I must say once again that I would no more deny "the existence of minds" than I would deny that fire burns and water wets. But this is not the point. The point is that if one does not know how to secure analytically this particular piece of common sense, properly and in a way that does not lead to irresoluble perplexities, then one will be tempted to secure it otherwise, for instance, by embracing the thesis of substantialist emergentism which, as we shall see later on, does lead to absurdity. To solve properly the problems connected with 'the existence of minds' thus becomes an effective "indirect" way of arguing against emergentism. The solution I propose will be found in Volume Two. Some of the tools for it, namely, at least a partial analysis of 'exist', I have readied in the first chapter. Now we have encountered the alternative "solution," which our analysis, if it is to be fully rounded, must both refute and deprive of its *ratio essendi*. Rome was not built in one day either.

2. With respect to (a) above, the analyst's contribution is to prevent confusions about the nature of definition from obfuscating whatever progress is actually achieved by scientifically more and more adequate definitions. We remember from the first chapter that quite a few of these confusions stem from the desire to make definitions as such the repositories of "meaning," in a sense in which it belongs only to the laws in which the defined terms occur. To safeguard "meaning," though in an entirely different sense of this most slippery word, is, as I mentioned once before (p. 141), one of the concerns of "holism." Emergentism, substantialist or otherwise, is but a variant of "holism." At this

point another line in the picture of the total dialectic becomes visible. It will impose itself as we add to the details of the picture.

The three propositions (1), (2), (3) in the text above state the thesis "realistically." To obtain a neutral statement, one merely has to replace 'physical object' by 'what is named by the proper names of the language'.

Some may have noticed that I am guilty of a slight inaccuracy. In the first chapter I insisted that the names of some relational characters will be undefined in any adequate language. Assume 'to the left of' to be such a word. If what I said is taken literally, then leftness is an emergent character. The level of "complexity" on which it emerges is twoness. Similarly, if the name of a certain five-term relation were undefined, fiveness would be another level of emergence. There are two reasons why I am rather undisturbed. For one thing, this is clearly not what the shouting is about. The complexities that supposedly generate emergents are of a different kind. For another, the very proposition on which I insisted and still insist, that some relation words are among the undefined descriptive vocabulary of any adequate language, is as it stands itself inadequate. From the viewpoint of technical logic it is outright false; for if one does not mind climbing up in the hierarchy of types (p. 43), then one can in a certain technical sense get along entirely without relations. This is not to say that what my statement intends cannot or has not been made precise. It has. But these are matters that do not belong in this book. Readers familiar with them can make the correction; those who never heard of them will still understand me.

Substantialist emergentism asserts that what "emerges" are not characters but "things." The rejection of this variant, too, is implicit in the rest of this work. My purpose right now is not either to accept or to reject but merely to understand clearly what is being asserted. The difficulty is that the "things" which emerge are either of a peculiar and peculiarly elusive sort, such as the so-called "entelechies" of substantialist vitalism and the "group minds" of certain sociological doctrines; or that they are peculiarly treated, as the emergentists treat minds or mental contents. The one way to avoid the difficulty is to choose an illustration that mentions none of these peculiar "things." Not surprisingly, such an illustration will be counterfactual and even bizarre. But that, we know, is rather a help. (1) Imagine that wherever and whenever there is a table there are at least four chairs around it, a flower pot on it, and a carpet beneath it. (2) Imagine an improved adequate language such that 'table', naming the kind it ordinarily names, is among its undefined character words. If our world were what (1) and (2) imagine it is, tables would be emergents in the sense I am trying to explain. The configurations from which they *may* emerge are, of course, a flower pot, a carpet, and at least four chairs in a certain spatial arrangement. I said may deliberately. I would have been justified in omitting it only if I had also imagined that (1') wherever there are a flower pot, a carpet, and at least four chairs in a certain spatial arrangement, there is also a table. But once again I must beware lest I become tedious. Everybody understands by now what is being asserted. Notice, though, that (1) and (1′) are rather specific cross-section laws. So is the last of the three propositions in which I explicated nonsubstantialist emergentism some paragraphs ago; only it is less specific. This will be our clue for the discussion of emergence in the context of reduction.

Since "holism" is a philosophical position, I continue to surround 'holism' with double quotes. 'Emergentism' I dismissed from this quarantine only after I had provided an ordinary meaning for it. Philosophical words with particularly potent associations I keep fenced in even after I have done this; for instance, 'realistic' in ' "realistic" language'. 'Substance' was once put to very crucial philosophical uses; some still use it "philosophically"; but many readers of this book will probably not be disturbed by such associations. So I did not bother to put a fence around 'substantialist' when I provided a clear meaning for it in introducing the notions of substantialist and nonsubstantialist emergentism. This is not to say that it is always clear what emergentists talk about when they talk about their peculiar "things." According to the one relevant explication of 'thing' I can think of, a thing is what is named by a proper name of the ideal language.

As 'substance' has been used by philosophers, "minds" are substances, mental contents are not. Historically, I thus committed terminological mayhem by applying 'substantialist' to both subvariants of "substantialist" emergentism. But again, these distinctions have faded; so the violence will do no harm. To Wundt the difference between those who acknowledged the "existence" of both "minds" and mental contents and those who held that only mental contents exist was still world-shaking. For him, only the latter were "scientists."

CONFIGURATIONS: EXPLANATION

The heading of this section is not true to its content. Nor could it be if I am right that there is no plausible employment for 'configuration' in the context of explanation so that its very use there creates confusion; a confusion compounded by the verbal connection between 'configuration' and 'whole', which latter, we saw, can be put to some plausible uses in the context of explanation. Somewhat perversely, the heading merely serves to emphasize this point and thus, once more, the distinction between the two contexts. Actually I shall fill the section with some odds and ends, all more or less related to process, that are needed to complete the analysis. Because it is so important, I shall first for good measure in the context of explanation expand what has been said or suggested before about 'configuration'. Second, I shall analyze what I called Wertheimer's mistake. Third, I shall explicate 'additive' and provide glossaries for 'whole' and for the formula that the whole is more than the sum of its parts. Fourth and finally, I shall say a few words about 'novelty'.

Take once more three test tubes, each containing a single stable chemical,

A, B, C respectively. Take next four empty test tubes; pour into one of them some of A and some of B; into another, some of B and of C; into a third, some of A and of C; pour finally into the seventh some of A, B, and C. Assume this time that marked reactions of some duration take place in all four tubes. (The "no reaction" case in the earlier story is really but a special case of process, namely, equilibrium, but the present assumption enlivens the story.) The four processes in the four tubes will all be different from each other. In particular, the process in the seventh tube, the one containing all three ingredients, will not be the "sum" of the processes occurring in any two or in all three of the tubes into which only two of the chemicals have been poured. (About the nonsensicality of 'sum' in this context presently.) There may of course be a composition law that permits one to compute the process in the seventh tube from the processes in the fourth, fifth, and sixth (I speak concisely. Besides, if there is such a law, the subsystems specified in its first clause, the one I called (a) (p. 133), need not be the parts in the three tubes.) Again, it is easy to generalize the example; the generalization merely restates what we know already. The process a configuration undergoes cannot without further knowledge be predicted from the processes any of its parts would undergo; for "as a rule" there will be interaction; and this independently of whether or not there happens to be a composition law. The exception from the "rule" is the case of closed subsystems.

Let us look at a psychological example. The master of a dog approaches him with a tasty morsel he can see and smell. We don't have real process knowledge of such situations; but we know that under ordinary circumstances the dog will run toward his master. This corresponds to the test tube with A and B. Another time the master approaches his dog with a whip in his hand. The dog runs away. This corresponds to the test tube with A and C. Still another time the master, in an experimental mood, approaches the dog with a piece of meat in one hand and a whip in the other. This corresponds to the tube with A, B, and C. We cannot from our knowledge of the dog's behavior in the first two situations (and nothing else) infer what he will do in the third. Certainly he will not both approach and flee his master, which is absurd. (The absurdity shows again how problematic the use of 'sum' is in such contexts.) The "holist" often talks as if the "elementarist's" so-called "logic" or "assumptions" forced him to embrace this absurdity. It would be an overstatement to say that such talk flogs dead horses. There never was a horse.

As to the word, 'configuration', there is only one intelligible use the "holists" make of it in the context of explanation. They employ it to emphasize interaction among the parts of a configuration (as I use 'configuration', in the context of description) during the processes it undergoes. This use of 'configuration' is expendable. We can instead speak either of interaction or of wholes; for this, we saw, is one of the clear meanings one may assign to 'whole'.

Though I have not yet cleaned up all the verbal untidiness, I have, I think, already destroyed the *mystique* of the whole. Wertheimer, I maintained, preserves it only at the price of confusing the two contexts. This I must now show in detail. His formula is "There are wholes the behavior *of* which is not determined by that of their individual elements, but where the part-processes (!) are themselves determined by the intrinsic nature of the whole." * I shall show by an example what this almost certainly means. (If one rejects emergence, as Wertheimer does, then it cannot mean anything else, except, again, interaction, which is nothing new.) Imagine two experimental situations of a kind quite common in the area of sensation and perception. In the first a human subject is presented with a small square of a certain color, C, in the center of his visual field and is asked what he sees there (description of situation 1). In the second situation, otherwise the same, the square is surrounded by a border of an appropriately chosen color (description of situation 2). In the first, the subject says that the color he sees is C (process 1). In the second, he says that the color (or shade) he sees (in the center of his visual field) is C' (process 2). The experiment is, of course, one in color contrast, the sort of thing the "elementarist" Helmholtz was interested in. There is indeed nothing in these situations the "elementarist's" so-called "logic" cannot handle. The reader should be able to "translate" without difficulty the psychological story into one about test tubes. Wertheimer disagrees. According to him, a change has taken place in the central square when it was surrounded by the border. Thus the bordered square is the whole whose intrinsic nature determines the behavior *of* its part, i.e., of the central square. Two things need to be said. First, if the two physical objects, the square and border, did interact, we would again be in the realm of process and the formula would not assert anything beyond interaction. Second, we know both from common sense and physics that the border has not in the least affected the square. Hence, nothing eludes us when we say in the context of description that the square remains as a part of the configuration exactly what it was by itself. What changes is merely the subject's response *to* the square, which is a matter of process.

Some, wondering how anybody could make so obvious a mistake, may wonder whether I have been fair to Wertheimer. I would observe that hindsight is easier than foresight. In some respects Wertheimer stands in the "phenomenalistic" tradition, to which so many of the classical British philosopher-psychologists belonged. (Only he also stands in other tradi-

---

* "Ueber Gestalttheorie," quoted from the translation in W. D. Ellis (ed.), *A Source Book of Gestalt Psychology*, New York, 1938, p. 2. Italics and exclamation point added.

tions; that makes the analysis of Gestalt so delicate.) Crudely speaking, the "phenomenalists" identify the physical object with the percept. Substitute 'stimulus' for 'physical object', 'response' for 'percept'; and you will see that Wertheimer merely consummates this tradition by confusing, as a scientist, stimulus and response. Of course, the suggested substitution jars anyone who is sensitive in these matters, since it jumbles, as I insisted one must not jumble (p. 19 f.), the science of psychology with epistemology. But that merely confirms my diagnosis and also exculpates Wertheimer. The point is that none of the classical psychologists knew how to distinguish properly between psychology and epistemology. (I have trotted out 'epistemology' and used it here instead of 'logical analysis' because I think it may serve as a tracer for some.) This should go a long way toward convincing anybody that I am not making a scapegoat out of Wertheimer.

The "philosophical" uses of 'additive' blur into those of 'elementaristic' and 'mechanistic'. The "elementarists," we are told, mistakenly take "additivity" for granted; it is, unhappily, part of their "logic"; thus they must neglect or even deny the "nonadditive" or "superadditive" features of "configurations" ("wholes," *"Gestalten"*). Let us see whether this means anything. For, as I had occasion to observe once before, if the indictment makes no sense, then the indicted cannot possibly be guilty. I can think of two and only two clear meanings one might assign to the new word. (1) One may use it to refer once more to interaction. To say that a whole (system of interaction) is nonadditive or superadditive is then the same thing as to say that its parts interact during the process it undergoes. (2) One may say that every theory with composition rules is additive. In this use 'additive' is synonymous with 'elementaristic' or, rather, with the one clear meaning that can be assigned to the latter. Neither in (1) nor in (2) does the new word serve a new purpose. At best it is superfluous. As the "holists" use it, it zigzags, very much like 'whole' and 'configuration'. Yet it adds to the old confusions a new flavor of its own. The flavor hails from another confusion, the failure to distinguish between 'and', the logical connective, and ' $+$ ', the operator of addition. 'And' stands between sentences; ' $+$ ' stands between numbers and only between numbers. Any other use of either sign is either derivative (definitional) or metaphorical or makes no sense. 'Sum' belongs with ' $+$ '; 'conjunction' (*Undverbindung!*) with 'and'. This is the key to the analysis of the formula 'The whole is more than the sum of its parts'. Presently I shall produce a list of the meanings that might be assigned to it. First, though, I had better insert the promised glossary on 'whole'.

As I mentioned earlier (p. 138), the confusion is increased by the circumstance that so-called vector "addition," the (c)-clause of Newton's composition rule, is written by means of a (defined!) ' $\dotplus$ '. E.g., let a_1, $a_1^{(1,2)}$, $a_1^{(1,3)}$, $a_1^{(1,4)}$

stand for the four vectors mentioned in the (b)-clause of the composition rule for the four-body problem; then the arithmetical part of its (c)-clause reads

$$a_1 = a_1^{(1,2)} \overset{\cdot}{+} a_1^{(1,3)} \overset{\cdot}{+} a_1^{(1,4)}.$$

Other composition laws, including those of the tentative and rudimentary behavior theories of Hull and Spence, are either of the same or of not much more "complicated" arithmetical form. This gives rise to the spurious criticism that the "elementarists," even when they try to make allowance for interaction, are yet peculiarly simple-minded about it. Sums, products, or, at most, weighted sums and products are all they ever consider! It is worth while to understand accurately why this criticism is specious, even aside from the fact that in their present stage those rudimentary theories barely justify that much arithmetical "sophistication."

In the discussion of 'theory' I mentioned a circumstance which I said one should note though we cannot explain it, namely, that the axioms of a theory state, more often than not, lawful connections among its more abstract (highly defined) terms (p. 33). To say that a certain lawful connection obtains among n characters is, in the quantified case, the same thing as to say that a certain arithmetical n-term relation obtains among the members of each of the (ordered) n-tuples formed from the values these characters have in an instance of the law. Now, modern logic has taught us that amazingly many "complicated" relations can be engendered definitionally from a few "simple" ones. In our world, the lawful connections among the less abstract characters are very "complicated." To judge from the success of theory, it would seem that they can be engendered from simpler ones that obtain among the more abstract characters. Strictly speaking, these remarks are still not an "explanation" of that remarkable feature of theories, namely, that the axioms state for the most part "simple" connections among "abstract" characters. Yet they help one to "understand." And they also throw new light on the supposed simple-mindedness of the "elementarists," in behavior science and elsewhere. Perhaps these theorists are not so simple-minded after all.

We encountered four clear meanings of 'whole'. 1. 'Whole' means 'system of interaction'. 2. 'Whole' may be used to refer to systems of interaction for which the composition rules of their parts break down. 3. 'Whole' means 'configuration'. 4. 'Whole' may be used to refer to configurations that mark a level of emergence. Uses 1 and 3 are nonspecific and therefore to be discouraged. Uses 2 and 4 are specific; most probably, though, there are no wholes in either of these two meanings. Meanings 1 and 2 belong to the context of explanation. Meanings 3 and 4 belong to the context of description. The German *'Gestalt'* is also used with all these meanings. Frequent shifts from one to the other, some intentional, some unnoticed, account in part for the fuzziness of the "holistic" arguments.

Now for the formula 'The whole is more than the sum of its parts'. Numbers are not parts of configurations. Taken literally the formula thus makes no sense. Nonliterally, there are two possible ways to give it some meaning; (a) one may take it purely metaphorically; (b) one may interpret it so that 'sum' comes to stand for 'conjunction'. (a1) The formula may mean that there are wholes in sense 2 above. (a2) It may mean that there are wholes in sense 4 above. (b1) The formula may be taken to mean that the law L of the process a configuration undergoes is not the conjunction of the, say, n laws $L_1, L_2, \ldots, L_n$ of the processes any n of its parts would undergo in isolation; in symbols, 'L' is not 'L_1 & L_2 & $\ldots$ & L_n'. As a rule this is indeed so. If it were not, the dog of my story would have to run simultaneously in opposite directions, just as each body of a Newtonian n-body system would at each moment have to move in $(n$-$1)$ different directions. The exception to the rule is, as usual, the case of closed subsystems. All the formula asserts upon this interpretation is, once more, interaction. (b2) is best explained by means of an example. Let D_W be the conjunction of the C- and S-brackets of a five-body system, i.e., a description of five bodies adequate to serve as additional premiss to Newton's process law. Divide (in your mind) the five bodies into two groups, one of three bodies, the other of the remaining two; and call their descriptions (adequate for Newton's purpose) D_{P_1} and D_{P_2} respectively. Our formula may be taken to mean that 'D_W' is not 'D_{P_1} & D_{P_2}' but 'D_{P_1} & D_{P_2} & X', where 'X' stands for the conjunction of the relational statements required to indicate how the two subsystems "lie relative to each other," so that we may know the initial mutual distances of any two of the five bodies. It is not difficult to generalize this example. Let $P_1, P_2, \ldots, P_n$ be parts of a configuration W; let $D_{P_1}, D_{P_2}, \ldots, D_{P_n}, D_W$ be the respective descriptions; assume that each of these descriptions is an adequate additional premiss for the application of a certain process law. Even if the parts jointly exhaust the whole (I don't think I need stop to explain what that means), 'D_W' will not as a rule be the conjunction 'D_{P_1} & D_{P_2} & $\ldots$ & D_{P_n}' but, rather, 'D_{P_1} & D_{P_2} & $\ldots$ & D_{P_n} & X', where 'X' is a conjunction of relational statements providing information as to how, metaphorically speaking, the parts "lie relative to each other." In special cases the description of the whole may be the conjunction of the descriptions of the parts. Closed subsystems are one such case.

The interpretation (b2) suggests still another one; more precisely, the latter is merely a special case of the former. It is both obvious and far-fetched, depending on how you look at it. It is obvious because its point is obvious. It is farfetched because it is farfetched to put so high-sounding a label on so obvious a point. According to this interpretation the formula means that virtually every interesting description contains at least one relational constituent (p. 149). No one disagrees and no one ever really did disagree. I, for one, am not aware that even the archmechanist Newton ignored the distances between the bodies. At the time of Wundt, though, in the special context of classical introspectionism, the point needed emphasis. The Gestaltists, though surely not they alone, provided this emphasis. Historically, this last interpretation of the psychological holists' use of the Aristotelian formula about a whole and its parts is therefore anything but farfetched. Of all this more in Volume Three, where the introspectionistic variant of the relations issue will occupy us for pages and pages.

Speaking loosely, as one ordinarily does, one will easily say that wherever there is a "whole," there is, according to the "holists," something "new." 'Novel' is just a more ornate synonym of 'new'. It is therefore not surprising to find 'novel' and 'novelty' among the words that occur rather frequently in a certain kind of argument. Another such word is 'unique'. Nor are the explications of 'novelty' and 'uniqueness' unrelated. For our purposes, though, it will be convenient to separate the two. I leave 'unique' for another occasion and conclude the analysis of "holism" with a few comments on 'novel'.

I can think of four clear meanings of 'novel'. (a) The new or novel is the process law of a system that cannot be obtained by a composition rule from the laws of subsystems. (b) The new or novel is the undefined character that emerges. (I speak concisely; thus I call the characters themselves undefined and do not set apart those that are "kinds" of "things.") With these two meanings 'novel' may be used to say that there are wholes in sense 2 or sense 4 of our glossary on 'whole'. Thus it serves no particular purpose. We remember, too, that whether there is "novelty" in either of these two senses is doubtful to say the least. There is novelty, certainly and quite uncontroversially, if the term is used with either of the two other possible meanings. (c) Let 'novel' mean first occurrence in time or, more precisely with respect to characters, first exemplification in time. Such novelty of defined characters is a common occurrence. The first model of a "new" car design that rolls off the assembly line is novel in this sense. (d) Take a class of systems and order them linearly by some criterion of "complexity," e.g., Newtonian n-body systems by the number n of their bodies. Select next some feature, say, an orbit's being a curve of a certain kind. There may be a number n_1 such that orbits of the kind selected cannot occur for $n < n_1$. (For an obvious illustration, if the orbit is to be an ellipse, then $n_1 = 2$.) As we ordinarily speak, we may say that the feature is novel in that it occurs "for the first time" if $n \geq n_1$. The notion is nevertheless not temporal. Our "elementaristic" analysis of process can account for novelty in sense (c) or (d) without assuming that there is also novelty in sense (a) or (b). For (d) I just gave an example. For (c) the chemical synthesis of a "new" substance provides an equally obvious illustration.

If names are desired for these two uncontroversial kinds of novelty, one may speak of *novelty through process* (c) and *novelty through complexity* (d).

REDUCTION

Can psychology be reduced to physiology? Can such group disciplines as sociology, economics, anthropology be reduced to psychology? If the answer to one of these questions, say, the first, is affirmative, is psychology really physiology? If so, is it misleading to speak and think of psychology as a science in its own right? The questions sound familiar, for they are much debated, and in a sense we know what they are about. Take the first. There is some connection between what we do and what goes on inside our bodies while we do it. The so-called reduction of psychology to physiology has something to do with this connection. That much is clear and to this extent we know what the question means. Yet its discussion is often rather confused. As with all fairly broad or general questions, the confusion stems in part from unanalyzed philosophy. The symptom of the intrusion is, as always, the "philosophical" use of some words, such as 're-duce' itself. Let me build a little verbal bridge. If psychology can be "re-duced" to physiology, then there is really no such thing as psychology. Thus there are really no such things as minds or mental contents or, for that matter, the "abstract" entities the behavior theorists talk about. There is nothing new in this; we know the pattern. But there is in this case still another source of confusion. Most of what is now being said on reduction is implicit advocacy, not only, as usual, of a metaphysics, but also of some-thing like a factual thesis. For once, the main culprits are not the philos-ophers but the behavior scientists themselves. In the reduction debate they air, confusedly and confusingly, some of their own disagreements. What, then, do scientists disagree on? Some would rather experiment; some would rather theorize. Some prefer to work in one area; some in another. Such differences are not really disagreements. Real disagreements within science are, in principle, quite unproblematic. Whether or not a proposed law is true is decided by experiment; whether or not it follows from a certain theory is decided by paper and pencil. The two kinds of disagreement I have in mind are not within science but, rather, about its future. For one thing, scientists may and sometimes do disagree on the *present prospects,* that is, the prospects at a certain stage of our knowledge, of certain lines of experimentation and theorizing. These are practical judgments, matters of strategy. For another, scientists may and sometimes do differ on the *long-range prospects* of certain kinds of investigation. To make such a judgment is more or less like maintaining what I call a "thesis." One's judgment may be colored by what he is interested in, particularly if he is not very reflective on such matters. Again, whoever is overly eager to "defend a thesis" will be tempted to use bad arguments; and bad arguments, on anything, blend easily into "philosophical" ones. All this has happened in the case of the two questions with which I started: Can psychology be reduced to physiology? Can the group sciences in turn be reduced to psychology? There is an analytical job to be done. Some of it does not depend on which particular science is said to be reduced or reducible to which particular other. It pays therefore to ask, more generally, what it means to say that one science can or cannot be reduced to another. Putting the question this way, one soon discovers that the notion of "a science" is not very precise. Its lack of precision is part of the blur that surrounds the question. This part, though, is rather harmless; at least it will not take us long to clear it up. Then we shall be able to see the precise question behind the blurred one, namely, what does it mean to say that one theory is being reduced to another. The end of a long discussion of the nature of theory is as good a place as any to take up this question. When I say theory, by the way, I mean process theory; for, with the exception of geometry, I know of no others.

The traditional names of the sciences are chapter heading words or, briefly, chapter headers. Like fillers, they are expendable. If the title page and the chapter headings were obliterated from a textbook of physics, it would still say what it said before; if 'physics' and 'physical' occur in the text, they either serve as fillers or can be replaced by words or phrases with a more specific meaning. The same goes for a work on economics or on psychology. But there is also a difference between a filler and a chapter header. The former has to be "specified" to mean anything; the latter need not and frequently cannot be made specific, yet it has some meaning. If an industrialist or a government official wants to consult a scientific expert, he will often without hesitation call for a physicist, or a psychologist, or a chemist, as the case may be. That shows that the chapter headers have some meaning. Sometimes, though, he will hesitate or ask for a combination team. That shows that the meanings of these chapter headers are not very precise. Yet they cause no trouble as long as they are used as they should be used, casually and without fuss. The names of the several sciences refer to certain groupings or clusters within our scientific knowledge. Nothing is gained by arguing where the boundaries between these clusters should be drawn or by trying to draw them as precisely as one may. This is the point. Nor is there nowadays much disagreement about it, certainly not among logical analysts. It was not always so. In the past, "philosophical" attempts were made to "define" the several sciences precisely. That led to all sorts of difficulties and confusions. For the last century or so the belief that such "definitions" are important can probably be traced to certain features of the Kantian metaphysics. This mistaken belief had some impact on nineteenth-century psychology. Some of the discussions between the followers of Wundt and those of Brentano, for instance, took the form of arguments about the proper "definition" of psychology.

Some wanted to distinguish the several sciences by their "methods"; some, by their "subject matter"; some, by both; these latter believed that each subject matter has its proper method. 'Method' is highly ambiguous. If it refers to specific procedures, such as the use of certain instruments, then the number of methods is countless and ever growing. Thus one would have to find a way to determine groups or clusters of methods. (The search would not get us anywhere. But I shall not show that in detail.) If 'method' means what is now often spoken of as "scientific method," two things must be said. If what is meant is a set of rules or prescriptions, like those in a cookbook, which if followed must lead to the discovery of laws and theories, then there simply is no such animal. If what is meant is that scientists make observations and, whenever possible, experiments; that they try to discover laws; and that they combine these laws into theories; then there is one and only one scientific method. Thus it cannot be used to distinguish among the several sciences. With so-called subject matter one might conceivably fare better. To see this, imagine that each descriptive word or, at least, each descriptive character word belongs to exactly one of two classes such that, while we know many laws containing words from either the one or the other class, we know none that contains words from both. In such a world there would be two sciences clearly and sharply distinguished by their "subject matter." Our world is patently not of that kind.

Once again I have taken the linguistic turn. So I shall use it to describe the clusters to which the names of the "several" sciences refer. Schematically speaking, such a cluster consists simply of the vocabulary of a theory. Practically speaking, it is often merely a group of words each of which occurs in at least one of a group of laws which we try or eventually expect to deduce from a theory. Or you may, if you wish, add the theory (schematically) or the laws (practically) to the cluster which, as I put it, is just a cluster of words. The schematic notion is, like all such notions, clear-cut. The practical one naturally is not; to try to make it so is foolish. I have on some earlier occasions spoken of areas. An *area* is simply such a cluster. Practically, this notion, too, is therefore not precise. As usual, I shall operate with the schema. The point is that even schematically the clusters overlap. Geometrical and temporal notions, for instance, will occur in all theories. Nor is that all. As far as I know, nobody denies, for instance, that there are *some* lawful connections between the properties of the things I see and either the states of my body or the percepts I have when I see them. Pursuing this line of thought a little further, we find it joining one we travelled before. Lawful connections of one sort or another are so pervasive in our world that one may well wonder whether there can be more than one really successful process theory about "everything"; or, if there are, of what special kind the "connections" among them would have to be (p. 101). This is indeed one way to arrive at the idea of reduction. Let me then state what it means to reduce one theory to another; for this, we discovered incidentally, is the precise question at the core of the vague ones with which we started.

Let T_1 be a theory, (P_1) its process law, C_1 and $S_1{}^t$ one of its systems and the state of this system at time t; analogously for a second theory T_2. I shall represent both 'C_1' and '$S_1{}^t$' by a single symbol, '$D_1{}^t$'. Then we have diagrammatically, as usual,

(a) $$[(P_1) \text{ \& } D_1{}^0] \longrightarrow D_1{}^t, \quad [(P_2) \text{ \& } D_2{}^0] \longrightarrow D_2{}^t.$$

A "system" with respect to a theory is, we remember, closed for this theory. What I shall say is easily extended to the often more realistic case of known boundary conditions. Nothing will be lost, though, and a lot of verbiage will be saved if we don't bother with the extension. Assume that there is a connection rule or, briefly, a connection between the two theories. 'Connection' is remarkably elusive, hardly more than a filler; 'rule', we saw (p. 136), is ambiguous and in some of its uses outright misleading. Yet I chose these words deliberately. Presently I shall make them cover three different alternatives, each of them quite specific and not at all either ambiguous or elusive. The point is that the conditions the "connection" must fulfill if we are to speak of reduction can be stated without reference to any of the three alternatives. Such, we know, are the advantages of a schema.

1. The connection coordinates to each $D_1{}^t$ one and only one $D_2{}^t$. In symbols, $D_1{}^t \longrightarrow D_2{}^t$. In words, to every description of what is a system in a certain state at a certain time by virtue of T_1 is coordinated one and only one description of what is a system in a certain state at the same time by virtue of T_2. Notice the asymmetry of the condition. It is not required that for each $D_2{}^t$ there is a $D_1{}^t$ to which it is coordinated. Some $D_2{}^t$ may not be coordinated to anything.

2. The connection coordinates no $D_2{}^t$ to more than one $D_1{}^t$. Thus a $D_2{}^t$ is either not coordinated to anything or to exactly one $D_1{}^t$.

3. Let $D_1{}^0$, $D_1{}^t$ and $D_2{}^0$, $D_2{}^t$ be connected by their respective processes as in (a). Then, for every $D_1{}^t$,

(b) $$\text{If } D_1{}^0 \longrightarrow D_2{}^0 \text{ then } D_1{}^t \longrightarrow D_2{}^t.$$

In words, if the process of T_1 carries one of its systems from an earlier (0) to a later (t) state, then the process of T_2 carries the coordinated system from its earlier (0) to its later (t) state.

When we say that a theory T_1 has been reduced to theory T_2 we mean that a connection between the two which fulfills these three conditions has been established. T_1 is called the reduced theory, T_2 the reducing theory. To understand the choice of the name 'reduction' for this relation between two theories, consider that, after a theory has been reduced to another, one can if one wishes dispense with the process law of the reduced theory. To see that clearly and in detail, let a particular $\overline{D_1}^0$ be given and perform the following three calculations. First step: Find the particular $\overline{D_2}^0$ that is coordinated to $\overline{D_1}^0$ by the connection. Second step: Compute from $\overline{D_2}^0$, by means of (P_2), $\overline{D_2}^t$. Third step: Find the single $\overline{D_1}^t$ to which $\overline{D_2}^t$ is coordinated by the connection. That there is one and only one such $\overline{D_1}^t$ and that it is the one into which $\overline{D_1}^0$ has been carried by (P_1) follows from conditions 2 and 3. Thus by using (P_2) and the connection one can compute $\overline{D_1}^t$ from $\overline{D_1}^0$ without making use of (P_1). After a theory has been reduced to another it becomes, in a sense, expendable. This is the heart of the matter. The diagnosis is confirmed by a further consideration. Let $D_{1,e}^0$ and $D_{1,e}^t$ be the descriptions of an elementary system of the reduced theory at times 0 and t respectively. In other words, $D_{1,e}^t$ can be computed from $D_{1,e}^0$ by means of an *axiom* of T_1. Let $D_{1,e}^0 \longrightarrow D_2^0$, $D_{1,e}^t \longrightarrow D_2^t$. As scientists speak and think of "reduction," they do not expect D_2^0 and D_2^t to be successive descriptions of an elementary system of the reducing theory or, what amounts to the same thing, they expect D_2^t to be computed from D_2^0 by means of a *theorem*, not by means of an axiom, of T_2. To see why this is so, consider that, thinking loosely, one may come to "identify" in one's mind the law that has become expendable (in this case, the law by means of which $D_{1,e}^t$ is computed from $D_{1,e}^0$) with the one that makes it expendable (in this case, the law by which the corresponding D_2^t is computed from the corresponding D_2^0). The one "becomes" the other, so to speak. An axiom of T_1 should in this loose sense "become" a theorem and not an axiom of T_2. (But one would not expect this to be so for the axioms of a theory such as, say, geometry, which is a subtheory of both T_1 and T_2.) Then one may feel, justifiably I think, that theory T_1 has been "explained" by means of theory T_2.

We understand now the appeal of "reduction." Next we must learn to appreciate how exacting the three conditions of our schematic explication of 'reduction' really are. Otherwise one might be too uncritical in his belief or too sanguine in his hope that reduction of an actual scientific theory of some scope and success to another such theory has actually been achieved or will soon be achieved. I shall offer some cautionary comments.

The record contains four cases or, as I shall call them, four situations in which reduction has been either actually attempted or is being talked about. Presently I shall list them and briefly discuss two of the four; but it will pay to submit for a little while longer to the rigors of an abstract treatment. So I merely observe for the moment that the schema I presented is in one respect quite unrealistic. As I stated it, the connection is *one-one* in the direction from T_1 to T_2. In each of the four situations it would be quite unreasonable to expect such a connection. The connections sought or claimed are all *one-many*, that is, a D_1^t is not coordinated to a single D_2^t but to a whole class of such, call it Δ_2^t. In symbols, $D_1^t \longrightarrow \Delta_2^t$. That this modification of the first condition requires one of the third is fairly obvious. (b) must be replaced by

(b')   if $D_1^0 \longrightarrow \Delta_2^0$ then $D_1^t \longrightarrow \Delta_2^t$.

In words, the condition is now that the process of T_2 carries each member of the class Δ_2^0 into a member of the class Δ_2^t. The second condition need not and must not be modified. If a D_2^t were coordinated to more than one D_1^t, we could not perform what I called the third step in the computation of D_1^t from D_1^0 without use of (P_1).

As long as we talk about a schema, we simply say (assume, postulate) that there is a connection which fulfills certain conditions. When we deal with actual scientific theories we must specify the connection. There are three different ways of doing that. (This, it will be remembered, is why I have stuck so long with the noncommittal 'connection'.) The three alternatives are again best stated schematically. I shall now describe briefly two of them. The third occurs only in physics, so I leave it for some later small print. *Definitional connection.* All terms of T_1 are defined terms of T_2. (I disregard again the terms of a subtheory common to T_1 and T_2.) Logically this case is trivial. As to the "connection," one obtains the D_2^t corresponding to a D_1^t simply by expansion, eliminating all terms of T_1 by means of their definitions. As to the laws of T_1, they are deductive consequences of the laws of T_2 and of the (analytic) definitions. In this case, and in this case alone, upon reduction the laws of T_1 therefore become literally laws of T_2. Logically, I said, all this is rather trivial. But it is not at all trivial to ask under what circumstances, if any, one could reasonably expect that a "definitional connection" between two substantial and substantially different theories will actually be a reducing connection. About this question I shall have to say a good deal in Volume Two. *Connection by cross-sectional law.* A configuration can be described in more than one way, either by attending to different parts of it or by describing the same parts in different terms. The following three assumptions therefore make sense. (1) Configurations of a certain kind can be described in two different ways, once in terms of theory T_1, once in terms of theory T_2. (2) Whenever the first description of a configuration of this kind is a D_1^t, that is, whenever the configuration is a system by virtue of T_1, then its second description is a D_2^t, that is, the configuration is a system also by virtue of T_2. (3) We know a cross-sectional law by means of which the D_2^t of a configuration can be inferred from its D_1^t. If a connection of this kind exists then the laws of T_1 are deductive consequences of those of T_2 and the cross-sectional law, though not, as in the case of definitional connections, of

T_2 alone. Again, the idea as such is not difficult; about the prospects of its being realized I shall have something to say in Volume Two.

I am done with the schema and ready to throw a quick glance at the world. There is not a single case on record of a more than temporarily successful reduction and only one, and a rather peculiar one at that, in which it was temporarily successful. This does not mean that we could have saved ourselves the effort of explicating 'reduction'. Since "reduction" is much talked about, particularly in the philosophy of the behavior sciences, and since it is our business to analyze such talk, we had to acquire a clear idea of what could reasonably be meant by 'reduction'. Nor will it do to be too scornful of the wishful thinking that so often goes with the interest in "reduction." The anticipatory character of this preoccupation is in the nature of things. It will often happen that we have a theory in one area but not in another or, more soberly, we may believe that we are closer to a theory in one area than we are in another. What is more natural, then, than to try a short cut by looking for a reducing connection? Strictly speaking, that makes no sense. One cannot reduce what one does not have. But if one is lucky, if I may so express myself, and hits upon the "right" connection, then one gets the theory one as yet does not have for nothing, as it were, from the one one does have. Nor is there anything logically wrong with the idea of such a short cut. How realistic it is is a different matter. It would seem that the more we actually know in either of the two areas involved, the more imperiously do the difficulties of an actual reduction, what I called the exactingness of the three conditions, force themselves upon our attention. This is the reason why I began this time with a schema and not as usual with an example, thus deliberately depriving the reader of the intuitive support he might have derived from one of the four classical situations. In this case such support has its dangers.

The four classical situations are the reduction of (1) thermodynamics to mechanics in nineteenth-century physics, (2) physiology (biology) to physics-chemistry, (3) psychology to physiology, and (4) the group disciplines to psychology. In Volume Two I shall devote a chapter to (3) and another one to (4). About (2) I shall say a few words now; for there is a lesson to be learned from this situation. (1), as it happens, is the one case I mentioned before, which was at least temporarily successful. Since it is rather technical and belongs to physics, I relegate the few comments I shall make to small print.

The reduction of physiology to physics-chemistry is part and parcel of the vitalism issue which once agitated both scientists and philosophers. The agitation has gradually subsided. But it is instructive to examine the situation that existed when it was at its height as well as what has happened since. One of the areas, physics-chemistry or, briefly, physics, was then in an admirable condition. Of course, we didn't have then, as we most probably don't have now, a single theory that was "final" and literally comprehensive of the whole area—whatever sense it makes to speak of literalness in connection with the inherently vague notion of an area. Schematically, though, we may imagine that there was a theory of this kind. In the other area, physiology, there was none. Nor is there one now. But there was a very large amount of all the several kinds of incomplete knowledge, that is, there were numerous laws couched in physiological terms, many of them very detailed, rather reliable, and impressive. In addition there were also many "connecting" laws, some cross-sectional, some dynamic, that contained both physiological and physical terms. What has happened since? As their knowledge advanced, "physiologists" tended more and more to state their findings directly in "physical" terms and to relate them directly to "physical" theory. There are two ways of describing this state of affairs. If one speaks and thinks loosely, one will be tempted to say that reduction has been achieved or, more soberly, that it is well under way. Strictly speaking one would have to say that since they no longer try to develop a real process theory in "physiological" terms, our "physiologists" have given up the idea of reduction and turned "physicists."

Many readers of the small print have probably noticed that the reduction schema is the same as that of the partial interpretation of a calculus (p. 37). Each statement of the reduced theory has a corresponding one or, as one so misleadingly says, a "translation" in the reducing theory, but *not conversely*. The "reduced theory" thus corresponds to the "theory" one hopes to construct; the "reducing theory" corresponds to the "calculus"; the connection is established by partial interpretation of the latter. This is the third possible kind of connection, the one I merely mentioned in the text. Because of the peculiar status of the "entities" of the calculus this is indeed a peculiar case. What needs to be said about its peculiarity I have said or, rather, suggested in earlier small print.

In the classical kinetic "theory," the reduced theory was thermodynamics, the reducing theory, aside from the peculiar status of its entities, literally Newtonian mechanics; each by itself an impressive structure of considerable scope and success. This makes the kinetic "theory" a genuine instance of attempted reduction. The initial success of this attempt was remarkable and even dazzling, one of the great triumphs of nineteenth-century science. But the trees of theory do not grow into the sky. After some time there were failures. In this particular situation, there is also a particular way out. One can "modify" the calculus (change the reducing theory) so that it "fits" the theory to be reduced. This is what happened then and has since happened again in the quantum theory. But in what sense, if any, can one then still speak of "reduction"?

Using words "philosophically," the "holists" often accuse the "elementarists" of "reductionism." "Holism" itself is supposedly "antireductionist." So we had better inquire what connections there are between the several specific issues behind the "philosophical" labels.

Assume that there are wholes in the sense of 'whole' I listed second in the glossary. In other words, there is by assumption at least one level of complexity such that for systems of this complexity the composition rules of a theory T_2 which is successful for their parts break down. This level of complexity may also be, though it need not be, a level of emergence. Consider first the case of nonemergence, that is, the alternatives (3) and (4) listed on p. 140. Take in particular (3), the case of an entirely "new" process law on the critical level. The difference between (3) and (4) makes no difference for what I have to say; but (3) is perhaps a little more suggestive; so I shall limit myself to this alternative. Assume furthermore that there is a successful theory T_1 for systems "on" or "above" the critical level. (The elementary systems of T_1 are configurations for which the composition rules of T_2 break down.) Could such a theory T_1 ever be reduced to T_2? Probably not. I say probably rather than necessarily because I cannot think of a deductive argument, in a schema, which would establish that to assume a reducing connection leads to a contradiction. Perhaps there is such an argument which I cannot see. Perhaps, on the other hand, one could construct a nontrivial schema in which there is some abstruse reducing connection between two such theories. However that may be, it is safe to say that the prospects of achieving reduction would be very poor under the circumstances. Notice, finally, that if there actually were two or more levels of breakdown then it would be very simple to delimit several sciences precisely. Each level of breakdown would be a sharp boundary between two sciences. There is thus some connection (filler use!) between "reductionism" and "holism." If the thesis of nonemergentist holism were true, then the prospects for reduction "across a level of breakdown" would be dim indeed. The emergentist variants of holism ("new characters" or "new things") are in some respects even more radical than the nonemergentist one. Some are therefore tempted to argue as follows: if there are emergents then there cannot possibly be reduction "across a level of emergence." It is important to understand accurately why this argument is fallacious.

As it happens, the distinction between the nonsubstantialist ("new characters") and the substantialist ("new things") variants of emergentism does not matter in this context. So I shall use the neutral 'emergent'. What matters is, rather, whether or not the emergents interact with the characters exemplified by the parts of the systems from which or in which (use whatever phrase you prefer) they emerge. Consider the following two alternatives. (There are others.) (a) The emergents interact. In this event the "level of emergence" is also a "level of breakdown." Thus we are back with the case we just considered. We know already that the prospects of reduction are very poor, to say the least. (b) The emergents do not interact and there is a cross-sectional law to the effect that each system (on or above the level of emergence) determines its emergent. In other words, if we know the system then we also know, by virtue of the cross-sectional law, what emerges from it or in it. In terms of the fable I told (p. 154) that amounts to this. Whenever and wherever there are a rug, a flower pot, and at least four chairs in a certain spatial arrangement, there is also a table (this is the cross-sectional law); but the presence or absence of this table makes no difference whatsoever for the behavior of the rug, the flower pot, and the chairs (this is the assumption of noninteraction). Assume now that there is a theory T_2 about the "elements," (in the fable, tables, rugs, flower pots, etc.) and another one, T_1, that contains the names of the "emergents" (in the fable, tables). Logically there is no difference whatsoever between the problems arising from a possible reduction of T_1 to T_2 and those of a case I discussed before, namely, reduction by cross-sectional law. The only difference is that this time some of the characters mentioned in the cross-sectional law are emergents. But that makes no difference for what is involved in reduction. It follows that under alternative (b) "emergence" would not have the slightest tendency to preclude "reduction." The mistaken belief that it would is but another instance of the confusion between the contexts of description and explanation. Emergence belongs to the former; reduction to the latter. Alternatives (a) and (b) correspond to what in the so-called philosophy of mind is known as interactionism and epiphenomenalism respectively.

Index

Abstract: and naming, 13, 18–19, 43; words, 17–19; meanings of, 18–19, 33; and existence, 37–38, 43, 53–54, 59, 96; in physics, 33, 37, 54, 159; in psychology, 54

Acquaintance, direct: and undefined words, 14, 32, 40; vs. perception, 19–20; and existence, 44; and certainty, 83. *See also* Acquaintance, principle of

Acquaintance, principle of: defined, 15; and theories, 32; in physics, 37–38; and existence, 44, 46

Action-over-distance: vs. mediation, 113–15; and field theory, 113–15; and time, 115, 130

Additivity, 138, 142, 143, 150, 156, 158–61. *See also* Holism

Analytic sentences: and synthetic, 26, 27–28, 68, 69; defined, 26–27; and "form," 27–28; and "meaning," 28; necessity of, 28; and definitions, 48, 49; arithmetical, 68–70. *See also* Truth; Tautology

Analytic-synthetic: fundamental dichotomy, 26–28

Anaxagoras, 100

'and' vs. 'plus', 70, 158, 160

Area: definition of an, 164

Aristotelianism, 53, 67, 84, 100, 127, 161

Arithmetic: as analytic, 68; and laws, 69–70, 72–73; and deduction, 69, 72

Atomism: in physics, 113, 141, 142; confusing uses of term, 141, 142. *See also* Holism

Augustine, A., 54

Axiomatization, 32, 35–37, 67, 72, 89

Axioms: of theory, 31, 32, 35, 49, 131, 159, 166; choice of, 32, 49; and definitions, 49; as synthetic, 49, 68; and scope, 131, 136; and process laws, 132; and reduction, 166

Behaviorism, 7, 36, 40, 54, 57, 62, 86. *See also* Psychology

Behavior science: and history, 9; and physics, 86, 90, 107, 123; developmental laws in, 95, 119; and process knowledge, 100–101, 110, 123; cross-sectional laws in, 104, 118; and statistics, 107, 122, 123; and relative autonomy, 110; group laws in, 119, 127; historical laws in, 128–29; and composition laws, 139; and holism, 145, 156, 157, 159; and reduction, 162. *See also* Psychology

Boundary conditions, 95, 114

Brentano, F., 164

Calculus: interpretation of, 37, 57, 71–72, 89, 91, 92, 107, 122, 123–24. *See also* Language

Cause: and law, 61–62, 66, 77; Hume's analysis, 62, 78; and time, 61–62, 105, 129, 130; meanings of, 61–62, 66, 127; as expendable, 62, 77, 78; 'real', 66, 77–78; and explanation, 75–79

Certainty: and 'analytic', 28; of logical deduction, 30; meanings of, 83; and new rationalists, 83–84

Chance, relative: thesis of, 121–22; and statistics, 122, 123–24; and be-